LIFE NATURE LIBRARY

THE PRIMATES

LIFE NATURE LIBRARY

THE PRIMATES

by Sarel Eimerl and Irven DeVore
and The Editors of LIFE

TIME-LIFE INTERNATIONAL (Nederland) N.V.

About the Authors

The Primates is the first volume in the Nature Library to have two authors—Irven DeVore and Sarel Eimerl. It could hardly be otherwise. The whole field of primate behaviour is a new and vastly exciting one—and it is developing so rapidly that the men and women most closely concerned with it barely have time to publish their own findings let alone put together the accumulated knowledge of the last decades. DeVore, a brilliant young anthropologist now at Harvard, spent many months observing primates in the wild; his further commitments made it impossible for him to write the book himself. (At the time of writing this, he is out in the field in Bechuanaland.) He agreed, however, to supply the information for this book, provided the text were written by someone else. This difficult task was undertaken by Sarel Eimerl, a graduate of Oxford living in the U.S., whose wide-ranging writings include a novel, a work of non-fiction, the editing of much scientific material, and magazine articles on a variety of subjects. To prepare himself for this task, Eimerl spent three months in California talking to such other eminent figures in the field of primate behaviour as Sherwood L. Washburn and Phyllis Jay.

ON THE COVER: Nibbling on a twig, a young orang-outang peers out of the gloom of a Bornean forest. Its dark skin blotches are natural, derived from the same pigment that causes freckles and other markings.

Contents

	PAGE
Introduction	7
1 What is a Primate?	9
2 The Monkeys: Success in the Trees	35
3 The Apes: Pioneers on Two Legs	61
4 The Rewards of Childhood	85
5 Life in the Group	104
6 The Group and the World Outside	129
7 Clues to Human Behaviour	151
8 From Ape towards Man	177
Bibliography	193
Credits and Acknowledgments	194
Index	195

TIME/LIFE BOOKS

Editor: Norman P. Ross

Text Director: William Jay Gold   *Art Director:* Edward A. Hamilton

Chief of Research: Beatrice T. Dobie

•

EDITORIAL STAFF FOR "THE PRIMATES"

Editor, LIFE Nature Library: Maitland A. Edey

Associate Editor: Percy Knauth

Designer: Paul Jensen

Chief Researcher: Martha Turner

The text for this book was written by Sarel Eimerl and Irven DeVore, the picture essays by the editorial staff. These members and departments of Time Inc. helped to produce the book: Patricia Hunt, Assistant Editor, LIFE Magazine; Larry Burrows, Nina Leen, Leonard McCombe and Ralph Morse, LIFE staff photographers; Doris O'Neil, Chief, LIFE Picture Library; Richard M. Clurman, Chief, TIME-LIFE News Service; Content Peckham, Chief, Bureau of Editorial Reference. This international edition adapted by E. W. C. Wilkins.

Introduction

In the last few years, great progress has been made in understanding man's closest relatives, the monkeys and the apes. New fossils have been found. Anatomical investigations have added to our knowledge of chromosomes, skin and nervous system. Biochemical studies have clarified the relationships of many forms of primates to each other and to man. But perhaps the greatest addition to our information has come in studies of behaviour.

Only a few years ago accurate information on the social behaviour of monkeys and apes living under natural conditions was limited to a very few species and, primarily, to the work of a single investigator, C. R. Carpenter. Recently, however, many scientists from several nations have spent months in the field, studying the ways of life of many primate forms. The authors of this volume have chosen to emphasize this part of the newer understanding of the primates, and to deal with social life as a way of understanding this order of mammals. The pages which follow are based on the latest accounts and, frequently, on information which is as yet unpublished.

The understanding of the social life of monkeys and apes gives many insights into the background and process of our own evolution. This not only has philosophic implications for the understanding of man but practical applications in psychology and medicine. For example, the importance of early experience in shaping the emotional make-up of adults is revealed by laboratory experiments on monkeys; how these crucial events take place in a natural state is shown by field studies. This combination of laboratory experiment and observation in the wild offers the scientist the rich insights which are described in this book.

At the present time, research on all aspects of primate structure and behaviour is proceeding at a rapid pace. Seven primate centres have been established by the U.S. government to accelerate understanding of the primates and to speed their efficient use in medical research. Several investigators are now in the field studying behaviour. A book such as this represents an exciting moment in the history of a part of science. It states new facts and insights, and at the same time makes clear that many of these will be further modified and enriched as science rapidly advances in its understanding of the relatives of man.

S. L. Washburn
Professor of Anthropology
University of California
Berkeley, California

1

What Is a Primate?

IT might, at first glance, appear surprising that the study of monkeys and apes should be considered as a subject worthy of a name all its own—Primatology. Here is a science that has within the short span of a few decades suddenly emerged as not only one of the most fascinating of all sciences but also as one of the most important—a discipline which has drawn to itself not only zoologists and biologists but also psychologists, physiologists, biochemists, and what is perhaps most interesting of all, anthropologists, in increasing numbers.

Why, we ask, should any anthropologist devote his career to it? Anthropology is, after all, the study of man; and anthropologists, pursuing man's own origins, would seem to have enough work on their hands without taking on the lower members of his order. The answer is that zoologists for many years have classified man with the primates because of their close anatomical similarity. Recent developments in the field of biochemistry support this classification by showing that close relationships of cells and blood also exist between man and all the other primates.

Now, thanks to a tremendous recent upsurge in studies of monkeys and apes in their natural environment, it is becoming clear that in their social behaviour,

A SHOW OF HANDS

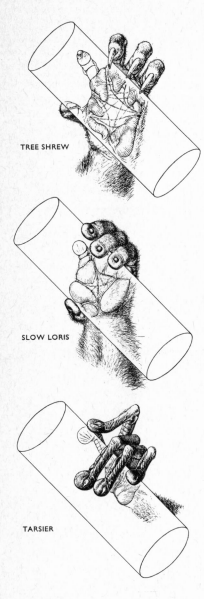

TREE SHREW

SLOW LORIS

TARSIER

While all the primates have hands with movable fingers, these often differ vastly in structure and variety of use, as seen in the drawings on these two pages. The primitive tree shrew has a hand that is little more than an elongated paw capable only of performing such functions as holding on to a branch by digging in with its claws. The hands of the slow loris have a highly specialized pincer-like grip. The tarsier, a jumper, has well-adapted hands with discs on the finger-tips that help it to hold on after leaping.

too, they stand much closer to man than anyone had suspected. Many live in highly organized and frequently hierarchical groups, some ruled by a single, all-powerful leader, others by a select group whose members pass down their power to their offspring. In a group of monkeys, some will be good friends, others dedicated enemies; some will be collaborators, others rivals; some will be popular, others despised. Infant monkeys, as they grow up, must learn a code of behaviour, much as a human child has to do; and all the members of a group are linked together by an elaborate system of communication which embraces both sounds and gestures and goes far beyond what is necessary for mere brute survival. The comparison with human behaviour, of course, must not be pushed too far. Yet in their daily routine and, in many respects, their relationship with their fellows, there are surprising resemblances between man and the non-human primates.

A CONSIDERABLE part of this book will be devoted to an account of what has been learned in the past decade about the social life of monkeys and apes. Possibly the reader will come to share some of the scientists' sense of fascination as they observed non-human animals in their natural environment behaving on occasion so much like humans that they might almost have been men and women in disguise. But to see the relationship between man and the primates in proper perspective, it is first necessary to understand what kind of animals primates are.

At once a problem of definition arises, because the order of primates embraces almost 200 living species. They range from creatures as primitive as the insect-eating tree shrew at one end of the spectrum to highly complex man at the other. And since the order contains the extinct fossil forms as well as their highly diversified descendants, no single characteristic, however basic, can be picked out as defining the whole group. Tree shrews, for instance, in most respects do not seem to fit in; yet they are included both on the basis of their ancestry and because of certain very specialized details of the skull. It can be said at best that what all primates, living and extinct, do show in common are adaptations for living in the trees.

These adaptations are many, complex, and in some cases very far-reaching. They show in the structure of primate brains and the possession of finger-nails and toe-nails and opposable digits; in the way primates use their senses of smell and sight and touch; in the way they give birth to and rear their young. No one species possesses all these features, but all show at least trends towards development of them—and these trends are characteristic of the entire order. And there is one quality which is shared by all the living primates except the tree shrews: the ability to climb by grasping.

Insignificant as it might appear, this talent lies at the root of the whole primate order. Essentially, primates are tree-dwelling animals. They came into existence in the trees; there they developed and prospered, and even today man is the only member of the order who has really forsaken them. And it was by the adaptation of wrapping their digits round a branch instead of simply driving their claws into it, as almost all other tree-dwelling mammals do when they climb, that the primates were able to make themselves the undisputed masters of the trees.

Their evolution towards this end proceeded slowly and from singularly undistinguished origins: from furtive, inconspicuous little insectivores which probably closely resembled the present-day tree shrews of Asia. Sixty million years ago these tree-shrew-type creatures were already living in the trees. From that period on, the story of primate evolution is very largely the story of how successive species improved their ability to move about in the trees. Grasp was the key because grasp meant security. It enabled primates to climb more safely along delicate branches and so expand their range of food. It reduced the risk of falling, and because of the superior purchase it provided, grasp permitted them to grow much larger than they could have done had their weight been supported by claws.

The process of transforming clawed animals into grasping ones started when the primitive insectivores developed long, thin fingers spread out in the first traces of a grasp. It was long debated whether or not these insect eaters should actually be classed as primates—the most recent tests for membership increasingly indicate they should. But there is no doubt about the suborder of prosimians which began to evolve out of them about 60 million years ago. German naturalists have described the prosimians as *Halbaffen*, half-monkeys, and the title is an inspired one. For prosimians are exactly that: they are a transitional stage between the insectivores on the one hand and monkeys on the other.

MARMOSET

For millions of years, prosimians dominated the trees. They spread across North and South America, across Europe and Africa, and on into Asia, ramifying, as they migrated, into a vast variety of forms. The fossil remains of more than 60 now-extinct genera have already been unearthed in various parts of the world, and there must certainly have been a good many others whose traces have not yet been found.

MACAQUE

Eventually they lost their mastery of the trees to the monkeys. Today there are no prosimians left in Europe or in the Americas, while the few which still survive on the mainland of Africa and Asia do so only because most are nocturnal animals which do not compete with the diurnal monkeys. One group of prosimians, however, made its way from the African mainland to Madagascar and a few smaller islands in the Indian Ocean—how, we do not know. There they found themselves in sanctuary, free of danger from monkeys or any large carnivores, and they evolved into several very distinct families. Today more than 20 species still exist, scattered throughout the island's forests. Fortunately, some closely resemble the early prosimians of 50 or more million years ago. So, by studying both the fossils and the living forms, one can obtain a fairly accurate impression of man's earliest fully arboreal ancestors.

CHIMPANZEE

ALL the Madagascar prosimians come under the general heading of lemuroids. Whether one judges them by their behaviour or their anatomy, they embrace a very wide variety of forms. Some move around by day, others in the evening, yet others only at night. There are primitive types, the size of mice, which live mainly on insects. There are more advanced species, the size of a large dog, which eat leaves and buds and fruit. Some are solitary, others highly social. And while the great majority of lemuroids are quadrupeds, the members of one family, the Indriidae, move in a unique style, holding their bodies vertically upright, even when they jump from one tree trunk to another.

Despite such variations, the lemuroids have a good many things in common. The mouse lemur, for example, shares many characteristics with other primates. It has a long, projecting snout with a moist muzzle, like a dog's, and tactile whiskers on each side. Its ears resemble a cat's. Its eyes are large and set quite close together in the front of the face. Unlike a cat's or a dog's, the fingers and toes are elongated and capable of spreading; and instead of digging its claws

Of the monkeys, the marmoset has the most primitive hands. Its grasp is awkward since its fingers all move in the same plane and must press an object against the heel of the hand. By contrast, the hands of the macaque and the chimpanzee are far more dexterous. Both are able to move their thumbs so that they can pick things up between thumb and finger. The chimp's thumb is shorter than the macaque's and thus inherently less efficient. But its brain is so much better that it can do more with what it has.

into the branch, as a non-primate would do, the mouse lemur grasps by wrapping its digits around it.

To watch a prosimian is, in a sense, to be transported back to the world of 50 million years ago. For it requires only a little imagination to perceive in these furry, bushy-tailed, transitional little animals the early forms of adaptation to arboreal life. Consider, to begin with, their eyes and snouts—the vehicles of sight and smell. To a considerable degree, these two senses are complementary. Both are methods of obtaining information, and the more use an animal makes of one, the less it will depend on the other. The balance is dictated by the way it exploits its environment. To an animal that lives on the ground and is active at night, smell can be extremely useful: it can identify objects not by looking at them but by sniffing them. To one that lives away from the ground and is active by day, the value of the sense of smell is lessened and that of vision is increased: this is seen particularly well in birds, whose sense of smell is as poor as their vision is keen. Even in the trees, the sense of smell is far less valuable than it is on the ground, and vision is far more; for it helps its possessor to avoid possibly fatal falls and also to identify food amid the rich and colourful foliage.

Just as natural selection in the arboreal environment favoured better grasp, so it also favoured vision and acted against smell. In a tentative form, the transition from reliance on smell to reliance on vision is apparent in a prosimian. Its snout is less prominent than an insectivore's. A slightly smaller portion of its brain is devoted to smell and a slightly larger portion to sight. This shift is reflected in the position of its eyes. Most primitive mammals have eyes set at the sides of their heads so that they can see over a full half circle without turning their heads. But this advantage is offset by an accompanying drawback. As their visual fields do not overlap, they cannot see very accurately in depth. To such an animal, the ability to judge distance precisely may not be critical; to an arboreal primate, it certainly is. As an adaptation to arboreal life, the prosimians' eyes therefore moved closer to the fronts of their faces, their fields overlapping somewhat and giving them vision in depth.

In any discussion of primate evolution, one inevitably returns before very long to considering how primates move—in other words, to how they escape from their enemies and reach their food. Locomotion is closely related to grasp, and it was in their ability to grasp that prosimians moved farthest away from their insectivore ancestors. They acquired highly movable digits, most of them equipped with pads on the inside and nails instead of claws on the outside on all but the second digit of the foot. But while they all secure their holds by grasping, the prosimians' actual modes of progress vary. Except for the upright Indriidae, the lemuroids use their digits to give them a firm hold while they move on all fours along the tops of branches, like monkeys. The African lesser galago, or bush-baby, by contrast, moves in long hops, using its back feet like a kangaroo. These creatures are amazingly fast, agile and accurate. A captive bush-baby once jumped 20 feet downwards to land securely on a door top, two inches wide, and on another occasion leapt from the floor to its owner's shoulder, holding a half-eaten mouse in its hands.

Other mainland prosimians, the lorises of Asia and the pottos of Africa, are as slow in movement as the bush-babies are rapid. Their method of progress is beautifully suggested by the native word for the potto, the "softly-softly". They proceed with considerable deliberation along the branches, sometimes on top and

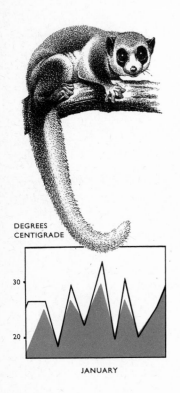

DEGREES
CENTIGRADE

30

20

JANUARY

UNEVEN BODY TEMPERATURE

Some prosimians, unlike the more advanced monkeys, have such rudimentary temperature regulating mechanisms that their body temperature is greatly affected by the environment. As the graph shows, the body temperature of the dwarf lemur rises and falls (black line) to conform almost exactly to changes in the surrounding air (coloured area). Thus when the environmental temperature is low, so is the body temperature, indicating decreased metabolic activity. During the cool season this lemur goes into torpor, living on the fat in the base of its tail.

sometimes underneath, progressing in undulating slow motion as they advance hands and feet alternately. In feeding, lorises will often hang by their feet with a grip so strong that they can pull themselves back up on a branch without using their arms.

There is another animal, the rat-sized, nocturnal tarsier, which occupies a unique position in the history of primate evolution. The living tarsier is probably the most specialized jumper of all the prosimians. Its legs are long and its arms are short. Its eyes are enormous; it relies much more on sight than the other prosimians do and much less on smell, and consequently the area of its brain devoted to vision is relatively large. Its snout is short and its nose is as dry as a monkey's. Clearly, the tarsier is not a typical prosimian. On the other hand, it certainly is not a monkey. Where, then, does it belong?

The answer is found in the tarsier's fossil forms. There is today only one species of tarsier surviving, on certain islands of the East Indies—but some 50 million years ago there were at least 25 genera of tarsioids scattered across North America and Europe. Their fossils show many features intermediate between the prosimians and the monkeys. It therefore seemed reasonable for a while to assume that tarsioids had evolved out of earlier prosimians, and monkeys in turn had evolved from tarsioids. This theory has now been generally rejected in favour of the belief that monkeys evolved directly out of fully prosimian ancestors more primitive than the tarsier. Nevertheless, the tarsier does probably offer some suggestive indications of what forms the earliest monkeys must have developed as they first began to diverge from the common prosimian stock, some 25 to 35 million years ago.

This assumption gains added force from the fact that it was not a change in the way they moved about but a shift in the relative importance of their senses that first set monkeys along their own evolutionary path. They came to perceive their environment in a new way. The senses and brains of prosimians still show many features of the primitive mammals. But in monkeys and apes the emphasis is changed. Just like man, they see stereoscopically and in colour, and a large part of the brain is devoted to receiving and interpreting visual stimuli. At the same time, they have lost much of their sense of smell—their snouts are small and they no longer have the prosimian's moist muzzle, and the area of the brain devoted to smell is radically decreased. Their sense of touch is transferred from the end of the nose with its tactile hairs to the hand. No longer do they walk with heads pointed down, ready to sniff at any object catching their attention; instead, they hold their heads up to take full advantage of their improved vision. And all these things are reflected in the structure of their skulls, with the greatly increased volume in the part which holds the brain, with the bony orbits that hold the eyes directed forwards and walled in on all sides to protect the all-important organs of vision.

THE great advantage of stereoscopic vision is that it enables its possessor to see clearly in three dimensions. This kind of acute perception permits man to manipulate delicate tools. It helped monkeys to see very clearly the branches they were about to grasp and also, buttressed by their colour vision, to identify any suitable food within reach. Relying as they did on vision, it was natural for monkeys to examine strange objects not by leaning over to sniff at them but by reaching out and holding them up in front of their eyes, which permitted a much more accurate appraisal.

To reach out and seize an object a short distance away may not appear a

TREE SHREW

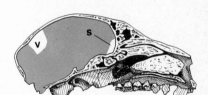

LEMUR

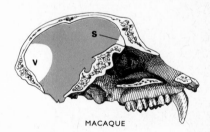

MACAQUE

BRAINS FOR SMELLING AND FOR SEEING

One important difference between the tree shrews, the more advanced lemurs, and still more advanced monkeys, is that the first depend primarily on smell and the others increasingly on sight. These characteristics are reflected in the brains of the animals, as these diagrams show— with the centres of vision marked with a "V" and the centres of smell marked with an "S". In the tree shrew, the smelling centre, located behind the nose, is relatively large. In the lemur it is small and in the macaque it is smaller still. The vision centres are just the opposite, being largest in the macaque.

HOW THE TARSIER
GOT ITS NAME

The tarsier is so named from two greatly elongated tarsal bones in its foot, shown in colour in the drawing below, together with the same two bones in the human foot for comparison. These long tarsal bones give the tarsier an added and extremely powerful leverage in jumping. Although it is about the size of a chipmuck, it can cover a distance of from four to six feet in a single jump.

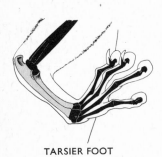

TARSIER FOOT

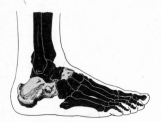

HUMAN FOOT

particularly demanding feat. We take it for granted because we are continually performing vastly more exacting tasks, such as threading needles or parking cars. But consider the problems it presented to prosimians. They had command only of what is called whole-hand control—i.e., while they could move their digits, they could only move them all at once, not individually. When they reached out to grasp a branch, all five of their fingers closed over it at once. When they reached out to pick up something, their fingers worked simultaneously in the same way.

Clearly, this way of grasping has its disadvantages—and the monkeys, as they evolved, improved upon it. In feeding, grooming and their other specialized activities, selection increasingly favoured refinements of control over the digits, to the point where at last monkeys were able to seize even very small objects with precision between their thumb and forefinger. This required a highly complicated set of interactions between the hand and the eyes and therefore a highly efficient controlling nervous system. And as monkeys kept improving their ability to grasp, their brains and nervous systems became increasingly elaborate.

Much of the increase in size of the monkeys' brains was devoted to areas controlling their hands and their feet, their fingers and their toes. Most of the remainder served to make their vision more acute and their memories more capacious. Monkeys, in consequence, became able to observe more intently, to discriminate more acutely between objects, to store up a vast and significant reservoir of visual images and to summon up, for comparison, a larger number of meaningful memories that could help them to handle the various situations they confronted. In brief, the monkeys were able to learn more—and therefore they required larger brains.

POSSESSED of all these advantages, monkeys were able to displace the prosimians, and they expanded rapidly throughout the forests. By about 30 million years ago, one group had spread across most of North and South America, while another had developed and spread across Africa, southern Europe and southern Asia. They had also reached their evolutionary peak. Many species were later to acquire new characteristics and specializations, but the monkeys' fundamental structure was set. And so, it might surprise the reader to learn, was the sensory system of the entire post-prosimian primate order, up to and including man. The human brain is perhaps a dozen times as large and vastly more complicated than that of any monkey, but most of this additional brain is devoted to memory, association and speech: that is, to abstractions. So far as his method of perceiving the world around him is concerned, man has advanced hardly at all beyond the stage reached by monkeys some 25 million years ago. He may not react like a monkey, but essentially he smells and tastes, hears, touches and sees very much as a monkey does.

Anatomically, however, men and monkeys are very different animals. Monkeys, being quadrupeds, retain many of the characteristics of primitive four-legged mammals. Their trunk is long, narrow and deep, and their limbs are hung from it in a very special way which restricts their movements largely to using their arms and legs in a forward and backward plane, as in walking or running. The general proportions of a monkey's trunk are much like those of a dog—and like a dog, a monkey tends to keep its arms and legs parallel. Even when stretching, it will reach out forwards, as a dog does when it awakens from sleep, rises, yawns and stretches out its legs. And in the trees, monkeys for the most part move the way a four-legged animal moves, walking or running along the top of a branch.

With apes, it is quite different—as it is with man. Unfortunately, the fossil record which would enable us to trace the emergence of the apes is still hopelessly incomplete. We do not know either when or where distinctively ape-like animals first began to diverge from monkey stock. The best that can be said is that they came into existence some 25 to 30 million years ago, somewhere in the forest that stretched at that time, uninterrupted by water barriers, from Africa across Asia to the East Indies. There are today four main genera of apes, divided into two families. One family includes the African gorilla and chimpanzee and their Asiatic relative, the orang-outang; the other family is that of the Asiatic gibbons. All are quite different anatomically from any monkey, and the most obvious distinction is that they are built for a different form of locomotion, with short, wide, shallow trunks that do not bend, and long, free-swinging arms which enable them to reach out in all directions in the trees, grasping and swinging their bodies from the branches instead of running on top of them, monkey-fashion, on all fours.

It is tempting to think of apes as being bipedal animals which are on the verge of standing erect and moving on their legs alone—but this is an oversimplification. Essentially they are still as four-legged as monkeys, but on the ground they move in a wide variety of ways, all of them quite different from the way monkeys do. The chimpanzee and the gorilla use their arms in walking —but they walk on the knuckles of their hands. The orang on the ground is simply awkward; it is almost never found there. The gibbon goes on two legs but balances with its arms held high. Only man is an efficient biped, and the structure of his pelvis and legs, which makes possible his characteristically erect posture and bipedal locomotion, is very different from the ape's—almost as different from the waist down as the ape's body from the waist up is different from the monkey's.

If the differences between apes and monkeys are apparent on the ground, they are just as clearly to be seen in their common habitat, the trees, by those whose eyes are trained to see them. The apes climb in a way quite different from all except a few species of New World monkeys: with their short, relatively inflexible trunks and long arms they reach out, swing and hang from the branches rather than running on top of them. In a laboratory experiment with apes and Old World monkeys both were given an opportunity to move across a horizontal pole and feed from small branches at the far end. Without exception the apes traversed the pole by swinging under it and fed with ease while on the ends of the springy supports. The monkeys, by contrast, ran on all fours along the top of the pole and fed only from a secure perch.

E XACTLY how or why the apes came to move about by swinging from their arms is debatable—but the most satisfactory explanation is that selection favoured arm-swinging as a means of obtaining food. Many branches high in the forest canopy are too delicate to bear even the weight of an average-sized monkey moving along them on all fours, let alone that of a big ape—but if the weight can be divided by hanging from several branches with two feet and one hand, then a lot of hitherto unreachable food becomes available. And this is the way apes do feed, in perfect comfort.

With the exception of the gibbon, all apes are much bigger than any tree-dwelling monkey. Obviously, the ability to swing from their arms provided

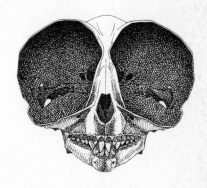

A SKULL FOR LARGE EYES

The most striking features of the tarsier's skull are its immense eye sockets, necessary to house its large, night-adapted eyes. If a man's eyes were proportionately as large, they would be the size of small grapefruits. Other odd characteristics of the tarsier's head, found in higher primates but not among most other prosimians, are protective walls of bone behind the eye sockets, and the positioning of the eyes so that they both look directly forwards, a requirement for stereoscopic vision. Among most prosimians the eyes are placed more on the sides of the head.

them with an opportunity for growth—but why was this opportunity exploited? What advantage did the apes win by growing bigger?

There was, of course, a competitive advantage: the advantage that any big animal has over a smaller one when it comes to eat or be eaten. But there is also the fact that size carries with it an advantage in the form of extended life span. Big animals tend to live longer because their rate of metabolism is slower than that of small animals: their internal organs simply do not have to work so hard, and therefore do not wear out so fast.

Any useful change begets more change along the line of development concerned: it is a basic rule of evolutionary dynamics. The practice of arm-swinging in the apes prompted a series of further changes which altered the primate anatomy, providing on the one hand the potential for tool-using man and on the other the extreme specializations of the modern anthropoid apes. In order to swing more effectively from their arms, the apes acquired a whole new complex of characteristics in their shoulders, their elbows and their wrists which combined to make their arm movements much more flexible. Apes can swing their arms out in a wide circle from their shoulders—forwards, sideways, backwards and upwards. With their more flexible elbows they can straighten out their arms, and their wrists are much more mobile than a monkey's—more so, in fact, than a man's. An ape can hang from a branch by one hand and rotate its body completely round, due to the flexibility of its arm and wrist joints.

Nor did the changes which sprouted from their arm-swinging stop at the apes' arms and shoulders. Ultimately they affected the whole of their upper bodies, giving them their characteristic short, relatively inflexible spine, the wide, shallow trunk with its resultant different arrangement of the viscera, and a pelvis splayed out to provide additional room for the attachment of muscles. All these changes helped to produce animals which, from the waist up, physically resemble man. From the pelvis to the skull, an ape looks and moves very much like a man, as one can see by observing an ape from behind while it is eating. Sitting there, reaching for food and carrying it to its mouth, it looks almost exactly like a man helping himself to various dishes at the dinner table.

For a variety of reasons, certainly including ignorance and possibly conceit, man has always had a tendency to consider his own qualities as being unique. In the course of so doing, people have tended to lump apes together with monkeys as animals that resemble each other, both physically and mentally, much more closely than either resembles man. So far as their intelligence is concerned, this assumption may be accurate enough. But as any close observer of apes and monkeys knows, man stands physically much closer to an ape than an ape does to a monkey.

It is important to remember that this similarity is primarily physical. Men and apes are very different, and man is no more the descendant of a modern ape than one grandchild of a common grandparent is the descendant of another grandchild. Still, just as a grandchild is linked to its grandfather by an intermediate parent, so man must somehow be linked to an ape-like ancestor. We shall be discussing this point in more detail in a later chapter. For the moment, it is enough to say that man, as he finally evolved, was the beneficiary of millions of years of evolutionary progress spurred on by the exacting demands of arboreal life. Although he long ago went his own separate evolutionary way, he has good reason to see in the anthropoid apes of today a vision of what his own ancestors may once have been.

THE GALAGO, OR BUSH-BABY, IS, IN VARIETY AND ABUNDANCE, ONE OF THE MOST SUCCESSFUL PRIMITIVE PRIMATES OUTSIDE MADAGASCAR.

Primate Beginnings

Primate, meaning first, is the name Linnaeus chose for the animal order containing monkeys, apes and man. From a little shrew-like progenitor in the Palaeocene, these creatures eventually came to dominate the animal kingdom. How the primates evolved—starting from the prosimians and ascending towards man—is a story which is now being revealed in ever new and fascinating detail.

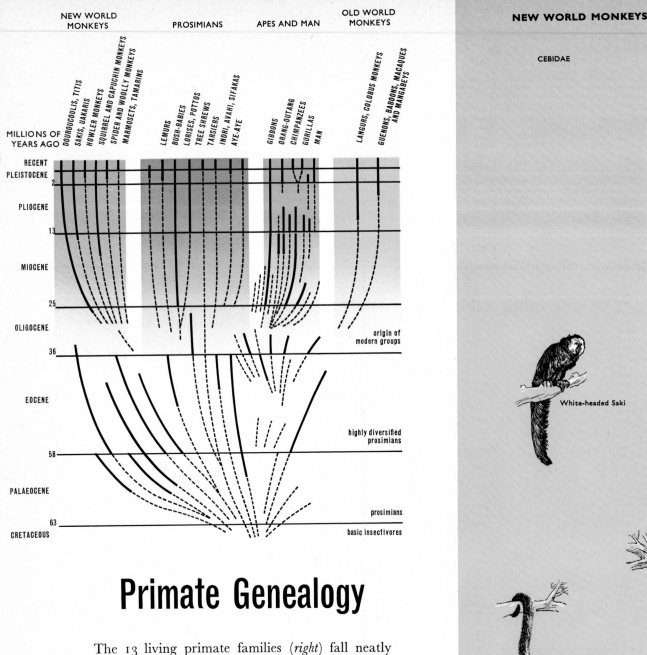

DOUROUCOULIS, TITIS
SAKIS, UAKARIS
HOWLER MONKEYS
SQUIRREL AND CAPUCHIN MONKEYS
SPIDER AND WOOLLY MONKEYS
MARMOSETS, TAMARINS

LEMURS
BUSH-BABIES
LORISES, POTTOS
TREE SHREWS
TARSIERS
INDRI, AVAHI, SIFAKAS
AYE-AYE

GIBBONS
ORANG-OUTANG
CHIMPANZEES
GORILLAS
MAN

LANGURS, COLOBUS MONKEYS
GUENONS, BABOONS, MACAQUES
AND MANGABEYS

MILLIONS OF
YEARS AGO

RECENT
PLEISTOCENE
2
PLIOCENE
13
MIOCENE
25
OLIGOCENE
36
EOCENE
58
PALAEOCENE
63
CRETACEOUS

origin of
modern groups

highly diversified
prosimians

prosimians

basic insectivores

CEBIDAE   CALLITHRICIDAE

White-headed Saki

Emperor Tamarin

Woolly Monkey

Primate Genealogy

The 13 living primate families (*right*) fall neatly into four main groups: green marks the New World monkeys, orange the prosimians, blue the apes and man, yellow the Old World monkeys. Each family is represented by a band, its width proportional to the number of living genera in it. Thus man, though boasting a larger population than the rest of the primates put together, has a narrow band; whereas the Old World monkeys, comprising some dozen genera, have a wide one. The chart above traces primate evolution. The solid lines are based on fossil finds; the dotted lines are guesswork. A fan of dotted lines rises from the common primate ancestor—a mouse-sized insectivore of which no fossil has yet been found. The Oligocene, where the fan breaks, marks a revolution. After this epoch of great geological change, the modern forms appear. Before it, all primates were crude prosimians, resembling the curious survivors pictured on the following 14 pages.

PROSIMIANS

APES AND MAN

OLD WORLD MONKEYS

GALAGIDAE

LEMURIDAE

LORISIDAE

TUPAIIDAE

TARSIIDAE

INDRIIDAE

DAUBENTONIIDAE

HYLOBATIDAE

PONGIDAE

HOMINIDAE

CERCOPITHECIDAE

ffed Lemur

Tree Shrew

Gibbon

Black-and-white
Colobus Monkey

Aye-aye

Man

Potto

Indri

Orang-outang

Hamadryad Baboon

Bush-baby

warf Lemur

Tarsier

Gorilla

THE PEN-TAILED TREE SHREW from Borneo and nearby islands differs from most other tree shrews in being nocturnal. As a consequence, its eyes and ears are larger than its cousins'.

THE COMMON TREE SHREW with its long bushy tail looks so much like the squirrels in Malaysia that local natives make no distinction between the two, calling both of them *tupai*.

TOOTH TO TOOTH, lesser tree shrews battle in a cage. Though little observed in the wild, such belligerence leads naturalists to believe that the contesting of territorial rights plays an impor-

At the Bottom of the Order

As their name attests, tree shrews were not always thought to be prosimians. Their general shrew-like appearance, coupled with their appetite for insects, caused taxonomists at first to lump them with the insectivores—the order which includes the shrews and moles. Today, however, in consideration of such traits as the bony rings surrounding their eyes and

tant part in their everyday lives. If these males were left in the same cage, one would certainly end by killing the other (the wound on the snout of the shrew on the right, however, is a cage mark). Tree shrews appear enormously wrathful, gluttonous and libidinous—excesses which anthropologist Carleton Coon describes as caricaturing "uninhibited human behaviour".

other primate characteristics of their skulls, these little South-East Asian mammals are placed by most experts at the bottom of the primate ladder. Still, they are a far cry from the most primitive lemur, one rung above them. With eyes set on the sides of their heads, they are poorly equipped to see in depth. Their muzzles are long, their noses moist, and they have no fully opposable digit. Tree shrews may be said, then, to straddle the fence between insectivore and primate; and herein lies their special interest. Though living millions of years later, all evidence points to their resembling closely that small insectivorous mammal which, during the Palaeocene, took to the trees and, by so doing, founded the primate order.

STARING STRAIGHT BACKWARDS over its long, brush-tipped tail, a tarsier shows the mobility of its head, able to swivel 180° right or left. Below it, a companion clutches a lizard.

The Tarsier: One of a Kind

The tarsiers, once widely distributed over most of the Northern Hemisphere, have dwindled to but a single living form that is now restricted to a few South-East Asian islands. Still, this survivor holds a number of primate records. For its size, roughly that of a rat, its enormous eyes are the largest in the entire order, and it also has proportionately the longest legs and largest ears. Eyes and ears are adaptations for nocturnal life, while its long and powerful legs are used for jumping about in trees, a startling form of locomotion, more like that of an arboreal frog than any sort of primate.

23

DISPLAYING INTENSE PLEASURE, A TARSIER SHUTS ITS LARGE EYES WHILE EATING.

A MOUSE LEMUR, ACTUALLY CLOSER IN SIZE TO A RAT, STRETCHES OUT TO SNIFF A CARNATION. PRIMARILY AN INSECT EATER, THIS LITTLE LEMUR

Lemurs Come in Many Forms

For the lemurs Linnaeus chose the Latin word *le-mures*, meaning "ghosts". And noisy ghosts they are for the most part, too, moving in a now-you-see-them-now-you-don't manner through the forests. But among the nine genera, all of them living on the tropical island of Madagascar, there is a wide variation in form, size and habits. The two pictured above, the five-inch mouse lemur and the four-foot-

tall indri, serve to illustrate the extremes. The little mouse lemur, though arboreal and able to grasp branches with both hands and feet, like any primate, is as much a quadruped as is its rodent namesake. It lives in nests where, during the day, it curls up in its long bushy tail. There, too, the female raises its young in litters of two and three.

The indri, on the other hand, behaves more like

ALSO FOND OF SWEETS, PARTICULARLY FRUITS, HONEY AND NECTAR.

LARGEST PROSIMIAN IS THE INDRI, FOUR FEET FROM HEAD TO TOE.

a monkey. Like a monkey, it sits in an erect posture, though its spectacular leaps through the trees on powerful hind legs resemble more the locomotion of a tree-living kangaroo. On the ground it hops along on its hind feet, holding its torso upright like a gib-bon. The female bears only one young at a time, which it carries along with it, clinging to its belly, wherever it goes. Socially, the mouse lemur is soli-tary and belligerent, staking out for itself a spe-cific territory and defending it ferociously against all other mouse lemurs; whereas the less solitary indri lives in small family groups. Finally, the nocturnal mouse lemur eats mainly insects, whereas the indri, one of the diurnal lemurs, feeds during the day on leaves, fruits and buds. A further variation of the lemurs' many forms is shown on the next two pages.

THE SIFAKAS, related to the indri on the previous page, share its agility in the trees and bouncy gait on the ground, but in place of the indri's stumpy tail they have long furry ones.

IN MID-STRIDE a sifaka shows why it is bipedal on the ground: its legs are long and its arms are short. It would be even more awkward for it to walk on all fours than it would be for a man.

CARRYING HER BABY like a money belt round her waist, a sifaka mother bounds off the ground with a powerful kick. A stunning cowl of white fur frames her naked black face and ears.

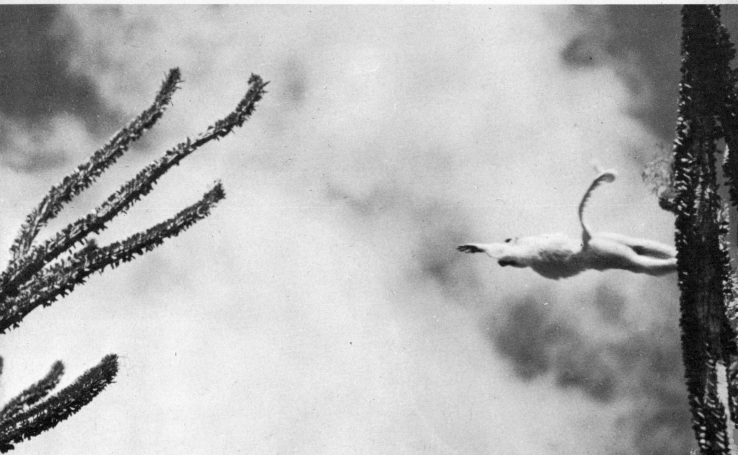

IN FLYING DIVES of 30 feet and more, sifakas show their common mode of travel. Here (*bottom picture*) a sifaka is caught at take-off, its powerful legs fully extended, its arms over its head like a diver's. In the top picture, leaping back again, it is captured in mid-flight as it twists round for the landing, swinging its feet forward to take the shock of impact.

ITS SAD FACE AND LUDICROUS CARE WHEN CLIMBING LED COLONISTS TO NAME THIS ANIMAL LOERES—A DUTCH VERSION OF DISNEY'S DOPEY.

The Lorises: Wide-eyed Sluggards

Apart from primitive tree shrews, the only sizeable group of prosimians to survive outside Madagascar and a few other islands in the western Indian Ocean are the lorisoids. These include the rapid-jumping little African galagos and the larger, slow-moving lorises themselves: the slender and the slow loris of South-East Asia (*above*), and in Africa, the potto and the rare angwantibo. By adapting to a life similar to that of a South American sloth, lorises have claimed an empty niche alongside their more active and intelligent cousins, the monkeys and apes. Sluggish in movement, solitary and nocturnal, they

28

ALSO FROM MALAYSIA, THE SLENDER LORIS (ABOVE) IS SMALLER THAN THE SLOW (LEFT) BUT HAS THE SAME NIGHT EYES AND STRONG HANDS.

feed largely on insects, birds and birds' eggs. In keeping with its torpor, a loris's metabolic rate is so low that even in the tropics it would die of cold if shorn of its thick coat. But slow as it generally is, a loris will move rapidly enough when necessary —when seizing prey, for instance. Unlike the sloth, which always progresses upside down, hanging from hook-like claws, a loris is as much at home on top of a branch as it is underneath one. It has an unusually long backbone with more vertebrae than any other primate, giving it the extra measure of flexibility it needs to bend around trunks and branches.

THE POTTO of West Africa, besides having the long and supple spine common to lorisoids, has an added feature: several vertebrae at the base of its neck protrude right through the flesh, forming a row of bony studs. Although no one is quite sure, it is supposed that these studs afford some protection for the vital spinal cord when the potto is curled up in sleep.

A POTTO'S HANDS have the most perfect opposition of any primate's. Where the index finger would normally be, there is only a vestigial stump, a modification that widens and strengthens the potto's grip.

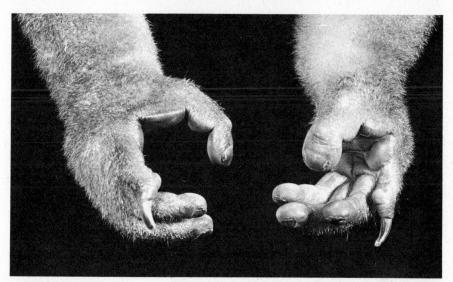

A POTTO'S FOOT shows the single claw on the second toe, characteristic of its group. Called the grooming claw, it is used to clean and comb the hair. Other digits have the flat nails common to primates.

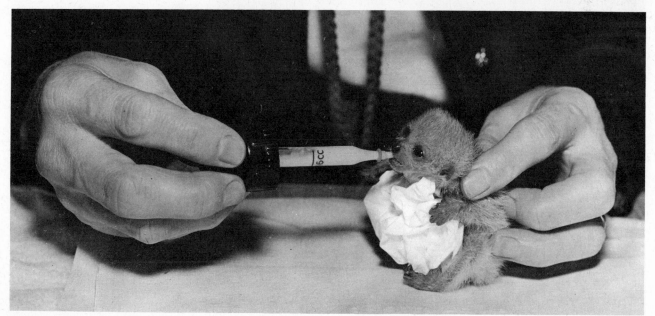

A BABY POTTO suckling from an eye-dropper clings tightly to its artificial mother: a crumpled piece of tissue paper. Pottos bear one young at a time, and from the day of birth the infant tenaciously clutches the hair of its mother's front. In that position it travels for the first few weeks of its life. This three-day-old female, born in captivity, was deserted by its mother.

COCKING AN EAR FOR BEETLE GRUBS, AN AYE-AYE TAPS AND PROBES A DEAD BRANCH WITH ITS SPECIALLY ADAPTED, LONG MIDDLE FINGER.

The Peculiar Aye-Aye

One of the most puzzling of primates is the aye-aye of Madagascar, so aberrant that taxonomists have assigned it a family all its own. Almost as large as its cat-sized body is its long bushy tail. Its teeth, made for gnawing, resemble a rodent's: they grow as they wear, taking a fine chisel edge. Its eyes, however, like those of many lemurs, are adapted to night vision and fitted with nictitating membranes which wipe them clean. Its nose is short, its ears are large, naked and protruding. Like all primates with the exception of man, aye-ayes grip branches with both feet and hands, but only their big toes are fitted with flat primate nails—the other digits all have claws. Like mouse lemurs, aye-ayes sleep through the day in nests, wrapped snugly in their ample tails. At night they use their specially adapted middle finger—incredibly thin and looking like a bent piece of black wire—much as a woodpecker uses its bill, tapping and probing for grubs under bark which they then rend with their strong teeth. In this nocturnal game of hide and seek their acute senses of hearing and smell are vital aids.

ITS PECULIAR CLAWS AND WIRY MIDDLE FINGER SHOW IN A CLOSE-UP OF AN AYE-AYE'S CRAGGY HAND.

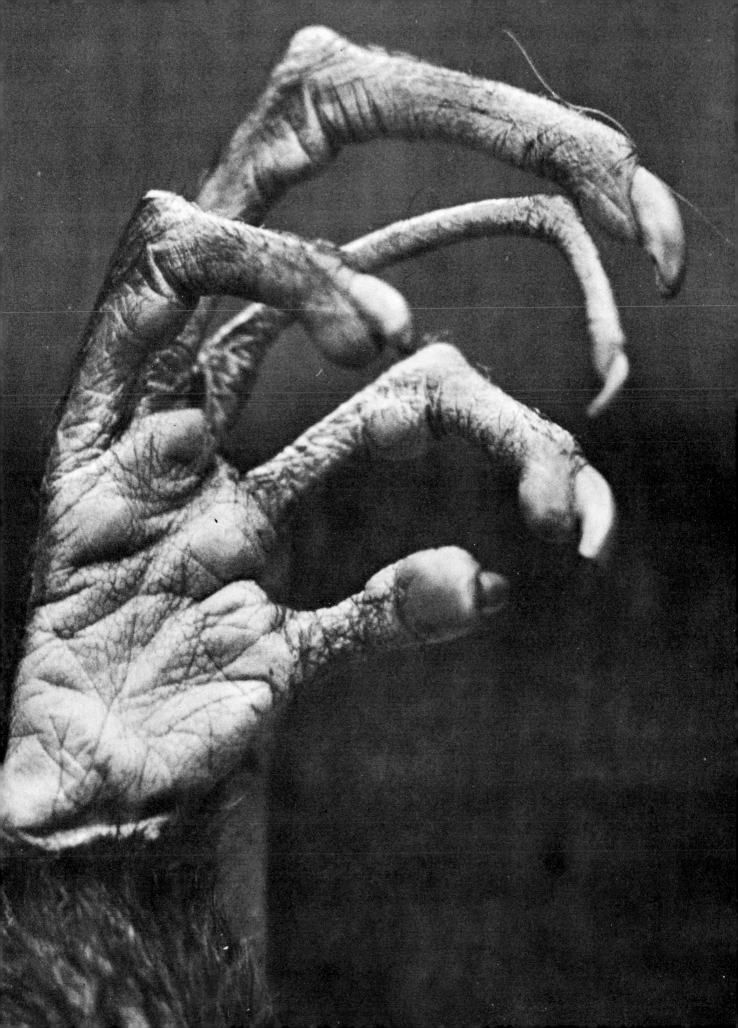

THE CAPUCHIN is the most familiar New World monkey, largely
for its winning way of soliciting
coins for organ-grinders. It is also
considered the brightest—perhaps
even as smart as a chimpanzee.

2

The Monkeys: Success in the Trees

Second only to man, monkeys are the most successful of primates. From the viewpoint of evolution, success is judged by numbers, and monkeys exist not only in vast numbers—many species in Africa attain a density of 100 per square mile—but also in a dazzling variety of forms. In South America there are monkeys no larger than kittens—in Africa, monkeys that weigh about as much as great Danes. Some are as timid as antelopes, while others will oppose a hungry cheetah and make it turn elsewhere for its next meal. According to the best available estimate, there are more than 30 genera of monkeys, divided into about 130 species. By contrast, men, though they have spread farther than monkeys across the earth, all belong to one single species.

Why is there so much variety among monkeys? One can approach the question at several levels, but it is easiest to begin with the differences which separate one closely related species from another. A species may be defined as a group of animals which is reproductively isolated from all other animals and shares a common gene pool. This means that the members of the group must not only be the same kind of animals—physically capable of mating with one another and producing offspring—but also that they must have access to each

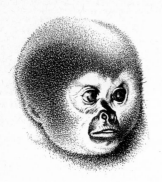

CATARRHINI
OLD WORLD

A DIFFERENCE IN NOSES

Monkeys from the Old World and the New differ in several, often subtle, anatomical ways, but one simple method to tell them apart is to look at their noses. The nostrils of the New World monkeys, such as the woolly (top), are round and separated by a broad nasal septum. This nasal structure causes the group to be called the Platyrrhini, which means "broad-nosed". Old World monkeys like the macaque (bottom) have narrow septums. As a result, their nostrils are close together, comma-shaped and pointing downwards; hence the name Catarrhini, which means "downward-nosed".

other. It is this matter of access that sheds some light on the amount of variety among monkeys. Many of them are arboreal animals which never, or only rarely, descend to the ground. Suppose the forest thins out or a stream widens into a river too broad to be crossed in a single leap. Unable to travel across the ground, the arboreal monkeys in the isolated set of trees will be cut off from other populations of their species. Generations pass; changes occur through mutation and genetic recombination, and those which are favoured by selection are passed throughout the isolated group, inducing perhaps a fresh dash of colour or a lengthening of the tail. Through time, these processes continue to increase the differences between the physically isolated population and the rest of the species, until eventually reproductive isolation is complete and a new species emerges.

Variations caused by selection are usually comparatively superficial at first; in fact, most closely related species differ primarily in their colouring or in minor anatomical features. These superficial distinctions have, over the milleniums, created the dazzling variations in design and colouring, in browns and greens and whites and blues and yellows, that are typical of the arboreal monkeys. The names of some of the guenons, the common monkeys of Africa, suggest the picture: the red-bellied monkey, the moustached monkey, the yellow-nosed monkey, the white-nosed, the spot-nosed, the red-eared, the white-collared, the green, the blue, the owl-faced. . . . How many species of guenons there are depends on which expert is doing the counting—more than a dozen is probably the best estimate.

Such counting of noses among monkeys suggests an interesting tendency: a genus that is primarily arboreal will tend to have a greater number of species than one that is primarily ground-dwelling. The langurs, for example, the common arboreal monkeys of Asia, number over 30 species. By contrast, there are only about one-third as many ground-dwelling Asian macaques, and some of these are island forms.

THE earliest primates were undoubtedly all very much alike. But the farther up the family tree we come towards the present, the greater the differences we find between the different groups in such characteristics as blood type, chromosomes, bone structure and digestive system. For time is a great divider, and its mere passage tends to operate like a wedge, driving deeper and deeper. Once one group of monkeys begins to diverge from another, the differences will inevitably be multiplied by selection as the milleniums pass. One basic separation apparently took place at least 30 million years ago, somewhere along the ancestral primate line, to produce two separate families today. One of these is found in Central and South America (the New World monkeys), and the other (the Old World monkeys) spread throughout Africa and Asia. Every living monkey belongs to one family or the other. The differences between the two are now very great, resulting partly from their long separation and partly from the effects of the environments in which they have lived.

If genetic change and selection are the father of evolution, environment and need are the mother. This combination has been responsible for every variety of life. For example, the most urgent problem an individual animal faces is finding food. It must be able to find as much food as it can digest or, alternatively, it must adapt so that it can digest the food that is available. Monkeys have solved this problem in many ways, and this provides a second answer to the question: why so much variety among them?

It is on the basis of their digestive systems that all Old World monkeys are divided into two subfamilies: one embracing the langurs and colobus monkeys, the other all the remainder of Asian and African species. The colobus monkey and the langur are primarily leaf eaters. Leaves, as a staple of diet, have both advantages and disadvantages. They are enormously abundant but they are not particularly nourishing. To extract the maximum nourishment from leaves, langurs and colobus monkeys have developed greatly enlarged stomachs. Both langurs and colobus monkeys have to eat such huge quantities of leaves to survive that after a full meal the food and the voluminous guts together make up a quarter or more of their total body weight. At such times a langur's stomach is so distended that even a well-trained observer often cannot tell whether a female is about to give birth or is just well fed.

THE advantage of the colobus-langur alimentary tract is that it enables its owner to digest mature leaves that other Old World monkeys cannot survive on. These old leaves even provide liquids. The Indian langur can go for several months without drinking water, and langurs in general can survive in drought areas where almost any other monkey would perish. Colobus monkeys inhabit the same trees in the Central African forest as mangabeys and guenons, and their digestive systems give them a competitive advantage. Suppose a group of fig trees starts to bear fruit. They will very soon be filled with a veritable menagerie of birds and animals: chimpanzees and baboons, mangabeys and several species of guenons, all busily attacking the figs. As the number of figs dwindles and the competition grows more intense, the monkeys and the chimpanzees might leave until finally all are gone. All, that is, except the colobus monkeys, whose specialized adaptation would enable them to obtain sustenance from the mature leaves that are useless to all the other monkeys.

There is yet a third reason for all these variations among monkeys. Consider, for example, the quite remarkable differences in physical structure and temperament that distinguish the colobus monkey and the langur from the baboon. Forgetting their digestive peculiarities for the moment, the colobus monkey and the langur are typical arboreal monkeys. Temperamentally, they are extremely timid, and their normal response to danger is either to hide or to flee. Physically, they possess a typical monkey face. They are lithe, long-bodied and slender, and their long arms and legs help to make them exceedingly agile. This agility is clearly an adaptation to arboreal life. A langur can run with ease along slender branches, race from the top to the bottom of a hundred-foot tree in a few seconds, and clear a gap of 25 to 30 feet separating one tree from another in a single, sure-footed, arching leap.

Baboons are very different. They are large, sturdy and powerful; full-grown males may weigh more than 100 pounds. They are not slender, they are not graceful. They are built not to jump agilely in trees but to manœuvre and fight. Their faces are much longer, with dog-like muzzles and heavy ridges of bone over the eyes. Their trunks are thick, their shoulders heavily muscled and made to appear even more formidable by a thick ruff of hair. They are clumsy in the trees, and leaping long distances from one tree to another would be impossible for them. And as for their temperaments, they are tough, aggressive, even bellicose, prepared if necessary to stay and fight against all comers except lions, leopards and armed men.

Why all the differences? The answer, in one word, is "predators". If food is the first requirement for survival, defence against attack is the second. To arboreal monkeys, defence is not much of a problem. Their chief enemies are carnivores, snakes, birds of prey—notably the monkey-eating eagle—and, very recently, man. In the trees, arboreal monkeys can usually evade a carnivore or a snake and, by staying under the top canopy, they can avoid most attacks by birds. A sturdy body and heavy muscles, and all that goes with them, would be more of a handicap than an advantage, since these would reduce the agility that is so enormously valuable in the trees. Almost all arboreal monkeys are, consequently, like the colobus monkey and the langur—lithe, slender, long-limbed—and timid.

To baboons, the qualities most suitable for life in the trees are of little consequence because they are essentially terrestrial animals. True, they sleep in the trees, often feed in them, and when threatened by lions, climb up into them for refuge. But most of their waking hours are spent on the ground, where they are in constant danger from predators: lions and jackals, cheetahs and hyenas. As an adaptation to terrestrial life, male baboons acquired long canines to defend themselves, their females and their young. As canines have to be fitted into the face somehow, baboons also acquired a long muzzle to house them. But animals which fight with their teeth need more than just teeth. They also need sturdy trunks, strong jaws and powerful shoulder muscles. Male baboons possess all these physical characteristics, and what is more, they frequently combine against a common enemy.

Still, hefty and muscular as they are, baboons cannot always be sure of winning a fight against, say, a leopard. Even if they do win, they are liable to get badly mauled in the process. Obviously they are better off if they can prevent predators from attacking, by bluff, perhaps—by giving the impression that they are more formidable than they really are. The ruff of hair around a male baboon's shoulders achieves exactly this purpose. It makes the baboon's whole body look wider and deeper, and thus helps to keep enemies at a distance.

For the female baboon, the picture is slightly different. She, too, is aggressive compared to arboreal monkeys; she, too, after all, is a terrestrial animal. But she is not really a fighting animal, because she and her young are defended by the males. Accordingly, female baboons do not possess long canines and are much smaller and lighter than the males. In fact, they are less than half as big.

Now, most male mammals are larger than the females—but twice the size? So vast a difference in bulk between the sexes—or sexual dimorphism, to use the technical phrase—can surely be no accident. And it is not; it appears to be the result of living on the ground. This is clearly demonstrated among the apes. Male and female gibbons, which spend all their time in the trees, are almost identical in size. Chimpanzees spend some of their time on the ground, and the males are somewhat larger than the females. Gorillas are primarily terrestrial, and the males are twice as large as the females. Presumably, the need of ground-dwelling primates to defend the group against predators has steadily resulted in larger and larger males. This is so for all the apes except the orang-outang. For reasons yet unknown, males of this tree-dwelling species are much larger than females.

Adaptation to environment also explains the existence of ischial callosities, those pads of toughened skin on the rump, just underneath the tail, in Old World monkeys. These callosities are related to sleep. An animal is most vulnerable while sleeping, and even the trees are not a completely safe refuge against attack. Certain snakes and carnivores, notably the nocturnal leopard,

PADS FOR RESTING

Among the characteristic features of Old World monkeys are the tough, callous pads on the rump, adapted for the long periods of time when these monkeys sit or sleep on tree limbs. Called ischial callosities, these pads (arrow, above) are formed on the undersides of the haunch bones and are flattened to make balance easier while sitting. Even if a monkey should wedge itself for support between a limb and the trunk of a tree, as shown above, the pads help to keep it comfortable, since much of the weight of the body is still borne by the insensitive callosities.

are competent climbers, and they can move both swiftly and silently. Monkeys therefore tend to sleep as far away from the tree trunks as they can, out on the most slender branches that will bear their weight, so that if a snake or a cat ventures out towards them, they will be warned by the swaying of the branch. But sleeping on a narrow branch presents its own problem: if a monkey just stretches out, like a man in bed, it is likely to fall. To ensure their balance, monkeys therefore sleep sitting on their rumps with their legs thrust upwards at a sharp angle, clinging to another branch for additional support. Because the pads of toughened skin are attached directly to the haunch bones, replacing soft, sensitive tissue between bone and skin, their owners can sit comfortably for hours.

Apart from baboons and possibly gorillas, there are only a few other genera of non-human primates which, when threatened, are able to stay and fight instead of fleeing or hiding. One of these, the macaques, lives in Asia; and although smaller, macaques are the Asian counterpart of the African baboons. They are also predominantly terrestrial and have acquired the same characteristics of body build and temperament for precisely the same reason: to defend themselves against predators.

A TAIL'S SENSITIVE TIP

The most dexterous prehensile tail of all the New World monkeys belongs to the nimble spider monkey (above). Truly an extra limb, this supple appendage seems always in use, strong enough to hang by and sensitive enough to probe for, feel, then pick up an object as small as a peanut (below). The tip, supremely adapted, has a hairless under surface with a pattern of ridges to give it added purchase when holding on—and also to heighten its ability to feel—much as do the whorled finger-prints of a man.

T
HE close similarity between baboons and macaques was largely responsible for the creation of a myth about monkey behaviour which won wide currency earlier in the century, and which continued to mislead anthropologists until its falseness was exposed by the field studies of the past decade. The myth is instructive because it can stand as an exemplary demonstration of the best possible way to reach wrong conclusions about animal behaviour: by studying them only in captivity. To understand why the myth blossomed so vigorously, it is necessary to recall for a moment the division of monkeys into the two groups of Old World monkeys and New World monkeys. So far as is known, the two groups evolved out of different prosimian ancestors and have been totally separated for at least 30 million years. Despite this, they all possess the typical monkey characteristics—a remarkable example of parallel evolution in action.

None the less, as one would expect, the parallelism is far from absolute. Several varieties of South American monkeys possess prehensile tails, each equipped with a patch of sensitive ridged skin similar to a human finger-tip. Although such a tail is as good as an extra hand, no Old World monkey has one. On the other hand, all Old World monkeys possess ischial callosities and no New World monkeys do. To a taxonomist, however, the most significant differences between the two groups are found in their blood, the patterns of their teeth and the structure of their brains.

These important distinctions between the two groups provided a reasonable basis for the myth—which ran somewhat as follows: Since *all* New World monkeys are anatomically quite distinct from *all* Old World monkeys, an equally clear distinction might exist in the way they behave. This argument was entirely theoretical since no one at the time had made a thorough study of even one species of either Old or New World monkeys in its natural habitat. During the 1930's, however, the American psychologist C. R. Carpenter did carry out a study of a group of South American howler monkeys on Barro Colorado Island in Panama, where observation is comparatively easy. Howlers, as their name implies, are exceedingly noisy animals, but as Carpenter found, they are quite amiable by temperament and rarely, if ever, get involved in fights. Meanwhile, several other species of South American monkeys had been studied in captivity and they proved to be equally mild and unaggressive. On the basis of this somewhat slender evidence, New World monkeys were judged to be friendly, peaceful and altogether admirable creatures.

We turn back now to the Old World monkeys. In the late 1920's, a group of about a hundred hamadryad baboons were placed together on an island in the London Zoo. Hamadryad baboons are distinguished from other baboons primarily by a particularly lush ruff of grey fur which encloses their shoulders like a cape and reaches almost to the ground when they sit. They are also different in their social behaviour: they form persistent groups composed of one male and several females and their young. The hamadryad male herds his females and is jealous of them at all times—even if one of his females is not sexually receptive—in oestrum—he will punish her if she strays and will certainly fight off any intruding male.

GIVEN these characteristics, the situation on the island in the London Zoo was an impossible one. The place was overcrowded to begin with, but worse still, there were many more males than females. With no chance of forming their accustomed groups, the males were bound to fight; and fight the captive animals did, regularly and with such ferocity that within a few years more than half of them were killed.

Most of the fighting naturally took place over the females. Once a fight began, the female would remain completely passive, covered by one male, while the other males surged around the pair. Furthermore—as was their natural habit—they constantly punished the female, grabbing and biting any part of her body they could reach. Every male who managed to win even temporary possession of a female promptly mounted her. The females' suffering, however, did not end with the incessant sexual pressure or with the bites of the enraged males. As long as the fighting lasted, the object of it was unable to break free and obtain food. Eventually, almost all the females in the group were killed, but even the death of a female did not necessarily end the fighting, since the males frequently continued to grapple over her dead body until the keepers intervened and dragged the corpse away.

The way the male hamadryad baboons behaved inside their enclosure suggested two conclusions. One was that baboon society was built on sex and jealousy. The other was that the males were themselves engaged in a continual struggle for dominance over one another. There was plenty of additional evidence to support this assumption. Even when no females were in oestrum and no fighting was taking place, some males showed themselves to be dominant over others, and they asserted their power with ruthless persistence. They seized food from the weaker males, threatened them, snapped at them sporadically, drove them into tiny corners of the enclosure and, in general, kept them in a continual state of terrified submission.

By an unfortunate coincidence, from the viewpoint of establishing the whole truth, the next detailed study to be made of Old World monkeys was carried out with a group of macaques which were transported from their homes in India to the 37-acre island of Santiago, just off the coast of Puerto Rico. There, it should be noted, they were fed regularly by human keepers. The macaques did not seem to fight with the savagery exhibited by the captive hamadryads. For one thing, this island was much larger. It had more room, permitting weaker animals to escape from the stronger ones instead of being hemmed in by them. None the less, the males were obviously in competition and used their canines vigorously in battles for dominance. The most powerful macaques monopolized the sexually receptive females, hogged the food, and just as the dominant hamadryads had done, brutally imposed their will on the weaker males.

Both these studies appeared to prove that baboons and macaques are ruthlessly selfish and aggressive and so determined to domineer that they will gravely injure or even kill any rival who tries to challenge them. On the basis of these studies, they were compared most unfavourably with the monkeys of South America. What is more, it was further assumed that the captive baboons and macaques were typical representatives of the entire subfamily of Old World monkeys. The conclusion was that all Old World monkeys lived in rigid social hierarchies, with the males competing viciously for dominance and the females occupying a status little better than that of slaves. Behaviour, it was supposed, ran hand in hand with taxonomy, and the whole world of monkeys was split neatly into two. The anatomically more advanced monkeys were all unpleasantly bellicose and existed in a state of permanent strife on one side of the Atlantic, while the more primitive but easygoing and peaceable South American monkeys lived together in serene harmony on the other.

The only truth in this delightfully well-ordered analysis is that some monkeys are more aggressive and concerned with dominance than others. But as the reader will presumably have guessed, the distinction does not lie between Old and New World monkeys; African and Asian tree-dwellers are just about as amiable and benign as South American ones. It does not even lie, as one might be tempted to suspect, between monkeys which are adapted to life in the trees and monkeys adapted to life on the ground. The true distinction lies between the baboons and macaques on the one hand and all the rest of the monkeys on the other. These two species have acquired to a greater degree than any others an adaptation which proved of great importance in their terrestrial living: a temperament enabling them to stand and fight predators.

How important this is—fully as important as long canines and big muscles— is evident from the numbers of baboons and macaques which populate the regions where they live. Numbers, let us not forget, are the mark of success in evolution, and in this respect the baboons and macaques are certainly the most successful ground-dwelling monkeys. There are, of course, other successful adaptations to terrestrial living: the gorilla, which makes up for its lack of aggressiveness by sheer size and strength, and the patas monkey, which instead of fighting runs away or hides. But the baboons and macaques are an illustration of how selection can work to favour not only a useful physical characteristic but a psychological one as well. And while this adaptation of temperament subsequently affected the behaviour of the individuals of these species towards each other as well as towards intruders of other species, it must be remembered that they never behave in the wild with the ferocity just described.

The vastly exaggerated view of baboon and macaque ferocity which was inspired by these two studies and was widely accepted actually arose from a failure to appreciate just how much a monkey's behaviour changes when it is kept in captivity. A captive monkey is simply not a normal monkey, and it does not even have to be kept in a cage for its behaviour to become abnormal. Whenever monkeys are subjected to unnatural conditions—when they are fed, for example, by humans—they are liable to become unusually competitive and aggressive. It is not hard to see why. In the wild, every monkey forages for itself, and competition over food is practically non-existent. But if a whole troop of monkeys is obliged to feed out of the same bin, any natural competitiveness they possess is inevitably exacerbated. The closer the confinement, the more aggressive they will be, just like humans, who are likely to be much more irritable in a large city than in the country, and very much worse in jail. Even comparatively peaceful monkeys, such as Indian langurs, are noticeably more nervous and irritable in confined areas around villages than they are in the roomy spaces of the forest. It is therefore well to remember that all conclusions about monkeys based solely on the way they behave in captivity, or when they are under any form of artificial restraint, should be regarded with considerable reservation.

The London hamadryad baboons and the Cayo Santiago macaques were peculiarly aggressive for yet another reason. In the wild, a monkey learns its place in the group as it grows up. By the time it is adult, it has established a relationship with all the other monkeys. They are all old friends, or at least old acquaintances. Every monkey knows that it is dominant over some, inferior to others. It is, consequently, the less likely to get into fights. On the rare occasions when a baboon or a macaque does join another group, it frequently gets involved in dominance battles which continue until its status is established, much as young boys do when they first attend a new school. It was therefore inevitable that scores of strange hamadryad baboons suddenly thrown together should have behaved viciously; just as with humans, when aggressive animals find themselves in a power vacuum, a struggle for power is unavoidable.

The adaptation of the baboons and macaques which makes it possible for them to stand and fight where others might run has enabled them to spread over much of the Old World—over a far larger area, in fact, than any other genus of monkey or ape. Adaptation to local conditions in this far-flung area, moreover, has led to the formation of well over a dozen species. This is a dramatic illustration of how aggressiveness may be related to the ability of an animal to extend its habitat; and it brings us back to the curious point, mentioned at the beginning of this chapter, that all the 150 species of monkeys between them have not been able to spread over as much of the earth's surface as the single species of man.

MAN has been able to range so widely for four main reasons. He is a terrestrial animal, not restricted to the forest. He can cross any natural barriers, such as deserts, oceans and mountains. He can live off a very wide variety of foods. Most important of all, he has developed culture, he has learned to make clothes and build fires which allow him to live in climates where he would otherwise perish. To a considerable degree, he shares the first three advantages with the ground-living baboons and macaques. They, too, can move over unforested land. They, too, can cross natural barriers such as rivers, because they can swim, which they do by paddling, rather like a dog. And they, too, can digest many kinds of food. Possessed of these advantages, a single species of baboon has spread across Africa from Dakar in the west to Ethiopia in the east, and south all the way to the Cape of Good Hope. Macaques have done at least as well. One species, the rhesus macaque, is equally at home in forests, in open cultivated fields and inside heavily populated cities. Another species, the crab-eating macaque, inhabits the mangrove swamps of Indonesia. Macaques range high in the Himalayas, and in Japan they dig for plants under the winter snow and pick up shellfish in summertime on the beaches. Were it not for the cold in some areas, for the oceans and the presence of competitors, they might well have spread over as much of the earth as man himself has done.

THE MARMOSET, SMALLEST OF THE LIVING MONKEYS, IS ABOUT THE SIZE OF A SQUIRREL. THIS PARTICULAR SPECIES IS FOUND ONLY IN BRAZIL.

Two Worlds of Monkeys

Monkeys, the most numerous and diversified primates, are grouped into two great divisions: New World and Old World species. Although they apparently evolved from different ancestors, they resemble each other, both physically and behaviourally—a remarkable example of parallel evolution. Fossils show they once ranged far into subpolar latitudes, but they are today almost entirely tropical.

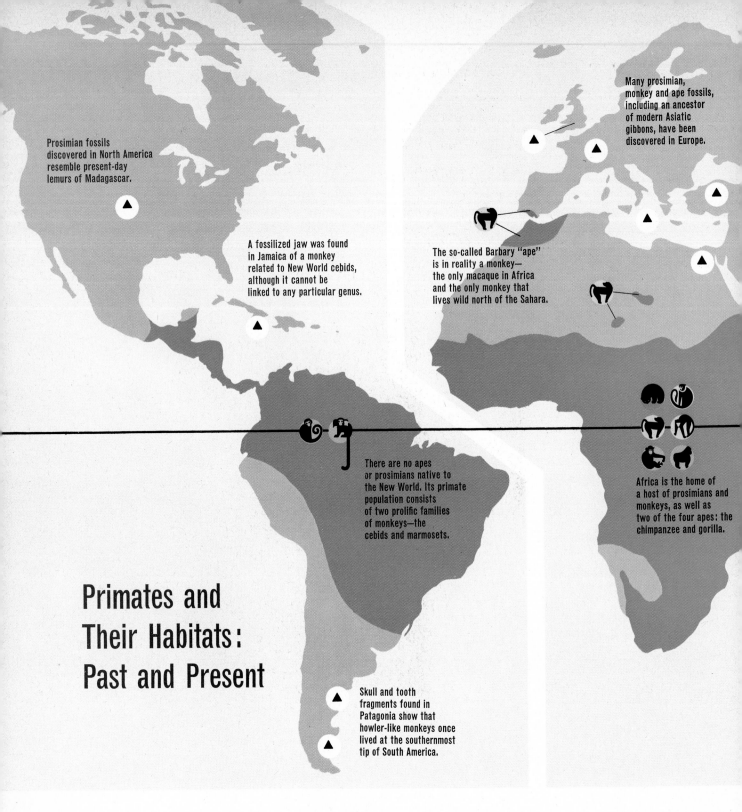

Prosimian fossils discovered in North America resemble present-day lemurs of Madagascar.

A fossilized jaw was found in Jamaica of a monkey related to New World cebids, although it cannot be linked to any particular genus.

Many prosimian, monkey and ape fossils, including an ancestor of modern Asiatic gibbons, have been discovered in Europe.

The so-called Barbary "ape" is in reality a monkey— the only macaque in Africa and the only monkey that lives wild north of the Sahara.

There are no apes or prosimians native to the New World. Its primate population consists of two prolific families of monkeys—the cebids and marmosets.

Africa is the home of a host of prosimians and monkeys, as well as two of the four apes: the chimpanzee and gorilla.

Skull and tooth fragments found in Patagonia show that howler-like monkeys once lived at the southernmost tip of South America.

Primates and Their Habitats: Past and Present

Monkeys are traditionally tropical animals. As this map shows, almost all of them are found living in a broad belt of hot rain forest or savannah running right round the earth roughly between the Tropics of Cancer and Capricorn. The key identifies the principal kinds of living Old World and New World monkeys, together with living prosimians and apes, each group given its own key colour. Closely related genera, even though they may live on different continents, are represented by the same symbols. Thus, the baboons of Africa share a symbol with their

cousins, the Asian macaques and the Barbary "apes". Similarly, African colobus monkeys and Asian langurs share a symbol, as do African pottos and galagos with Asian lorises. The small black triangles denote places where important fossil finds have been made outside the tropics, indicating how much more widely spread primates once were than they are today.

This former wider distribution is due, of course, to the much warmer climate that prevailed in past ages which permitted tropical forest to spread over much of the earth. But about

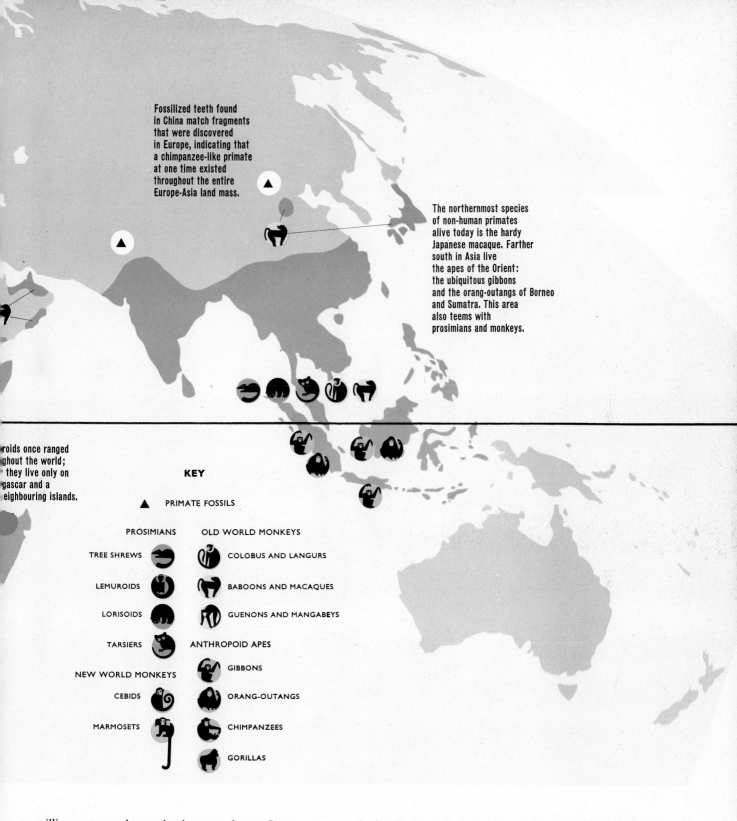

Fossilized teeth found in China match fragments that were discovered in Europe, indicating that a chimpanzee-like primate at one time existed throughout the entire Europe-Asia land mass.

The northernmost species of non-human primates alive today is the hardy Japanese macaque. Farther south in Asia live the apes of the Orient: the ubiquitous gibbons and the orang-outangs of Borneo and Sumatra. This area also teems with prosimians and monkeys.

...roids once ranged ...ghout the world; ... they live only on ...gascar and a ...eighbouring islands.

KEY

▲ PRIMATE FOSSILS

PROSIMIANS   OLD WORLD MONKEYS
TREE SHREWS   COLOBUS AND LANGURS
LEMUROIDS   BABOONS AND MACAQUES
LORISOIDS   GUENONS AND MANGABEYS
TARSIERS   ANTHROPOID APES
NEW WORLD MONKEYS   GIBBONS
CEBIDS   ORANG-OUTANGS
MARMOSETS   CHIMPANZEES
                      GORILLAS

35 million years ago the weather began to change. In response to long periods of cold and dryness, the tropical forests shrank until they were restricted to the essentially equatorial position they occupy today. During this period a few of the monkeys—notably the baboons and macaques—left the heavy forest and gradually became adjusted to living on the open savannah. But where the forests survived, most primates stayed in the trees.

Scientists are hoping that the climatic changes of the ancient earth will, as they are better understood, help to explain the distribution and relationships of the various different kinds of primates. It is clear, for example, that the African forests that contain colobus monkeys were once connected to the Asian forests that contain their close cousins, the langurs. What is not so clear is when the ancestors of the New World monkeys and the Old World monkeys became separated. One thing that is certain is that this took place long before the evolution of apes, for there are no apes in South America, only large local monkeys that fill by default the niches occupied by apes elsewhere.

Gripping Tails of the Jungle

There are some 65 species of New World monkeys. Many of these have a very useful anatomical adaptation lacking in their Old World counterparts: that curious "fifth hand", the prehensile tail. And in a few species, like those on this page, the gripping tail has developed to such an extent that it actually has "finger-prints" on the tip. While of course a tail is not equipped with fingers, it can sometimes be even more useful than an arm or a leg. A spider monkey's tail, for instance, is longer than its head and body combined, and is frequently used instead of a hand to grasp distant objects. Other monkeys less fortunate are forced to relegate at least one limb to support while they feed, whereas monkeys endowed with prehensility can hang by their tails while they feast with both hands and feet. A few New World monkeys have also evolved arms and shoulders that are suitable for swinging hand over hand through the trees like the Asiatic gibbons.

WOOLLY MONKEY

RED HOWLER MONKEY

BLACK HOWLER MONKEY

DER MONKEY GRASPS A TREE TRUNK WITH ITS POWERFUL PREHENSILE TAIL.

47

OUT ON A LIMB, squirrel monkeys are seen in their typical habitat: high, thick growth in the trees. Their long, heavy tails are not in the least prehensile but are useful for maintaining balance in jumps.

LUNCH IN HAND, a squirrel monkey prepares to devour a large insect it has captured. Protein-rich insects supplement its normal fruit diet. At times it will add a small bird to its menu as a special titbit.

NEW WORLD MONKEYS

The Prolific Squirrel Monkeys

If sheer numbers can be used as a criterion, squirrel monkeys are extremely successful creatures, even though their lack of a prehensile tail technically categorizes them as less advanced than their five-limbed cousins. They often travel in large troops with hundreds of individuals, and the troops themselves are so numerous that there are usually at least two within sight of each other at all times. Their activities are usually centred around a water source, where lush growth gives them a highly specialized ecological niche: trees decked with vines bearing a great variety of edible flowers and fruit.

TRAPPED ON THE GROUND, a squirrel monkey is crushed by a rainbow boa. In trees these monkeys are unmolested except by an occasional eagle, but on the ground they are vulnerable.

IN A RARE ACROBATIC MOMENT, A UAKARI LEAPS ACROSS A FOREST ABYSS. IT USUALLY GOES SLOWLY ALONG BRANCHES ON ALL FOURS.

AN INVERTED UAKARI hangs by its feet from a branch. Since little is known of its habits, no one can say what this animal is doing, but uakaris are known to walk upright sometimes.

NEW WORLD MONKEYS

The Mysterious Uakari

One of the rarest of the New World monkeys is the uakari, a cat-sized creature with a short, non-prehensile tail. It lives only in a few isolated areas along the banks of large Amazonian rivers and has adapted to life in the highest tree branches, rarely if ever descending to the ground. Uakaris are hunted by Indians of the area; adults are eaten, but young ones are usually kept as pets.

Short of tail and with sparse, unkempt hair, they move slowly in the trees. Their facial expression seems to be one of constant sorrow—but their emotions are betrayed by the colour of the bare skin on their heads and faces. It is normally a rosy pink, but in times of excitement or anger it flushes to crimson.

A BABY UAKARI clings to its mother. Despite their surprising habit of emitting what sounds like hysterical laughter when annoyed, these creatures are reputed to make delightful pets when they are young—so loyal to their owners that if deserted they refuse all food and ultimately pine away. As adults, however, they are less tractable and do not adjust well to captivity.

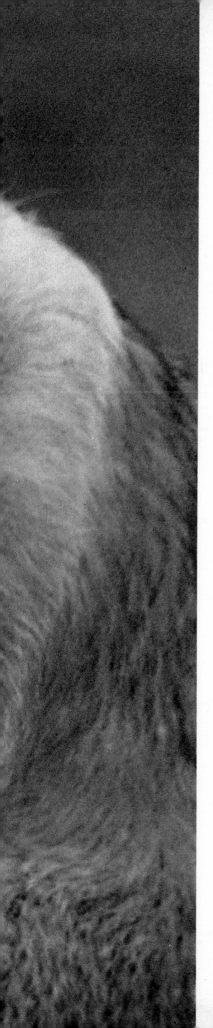

HOLDING ON WITH ONE HAND, A PROBOSCIS MONKEY DRINKS WITH THE OTHER.

OLD WORLD MONKEYS

A Primate Pinocchio

Old World monkeys are more uniform in their behaviour than New World monkeys, but they vary greatly in size and appearance. One of the most bizarre is the proboscis monkey, an aptly named species of langur found in the forests of Borneo. Since the bulbous nose occurs only in adult males, it is probably the result of sexual selection—i.e., through the course of evolution, females preferred the males with the largest noses. These odd monkeys delight in swimming: a favourite escape from midday heat is to drop into a stream and thrash about with a crude dog paddle. They often live in large troops. Individually, they are calm of temperament. Another member of the family, the snub-nosed langur, has a nose permanently upturned.

THE PEAR-SHAPED NOSE of a proboscis monkey surprisingly does not get in the way while its owner eats. Like all langurs, these are leaf-eaters, but they also eat palm shoots and fruit.

THE **STRIKING PELT** of the black-and-white colobus monkey was coveted by Abyssinian natives and European ladies alike. Two million were killed before the rage declined—just in time to save the species from extinction.

THE **GOLDEN LANGUR** changes its colour with the seasons. It is creamy white in summer, but in cold weather it turns to a light chestnut or golden hue.

The Timid Leaf-Eaters

The colobus monkeys of Africa and their rare Asian cousin the golden langur are retiring creatures that live deep in the virgin forest and rarely come in contact with human beings. The entire subfamily of colobus monkeys and langurs, which includes the proboscis monkeys, exists solely on vegetation. The enormous quantity of leaves that they eat has led to the development of a specialized labyrinthine stomach that can extract the greatest possible nourishment from the unnutritive bulk.

The golden langur is such a recluse that, although it was rumoured to exist in 1907, nobody was able to track it down and obtain specimens and photographic proof until 1953. Its Indian relatives, the common langurs, however, are not strangers to mankind. They are notorious for raiding crops but are tolerated because they are held to be sacred to the god Hanuman. They have the privilege of living on the grounds of Hindu temples.

KIRK'S RED COLOBUS MONKEY LIVES IN A REMOTE SECTION OF ZANZIBAR. ONLY ABOUT 200 ARE ALIVE TODAY.

RED-EARED GUENON

SCHMIDT'S WHITE-NOSED MONKEY

The Madcap Guenons

The guenons of Africa make up one of the largest groups in the primate world. All told, they include about a hundred different varieties, with immense diversity in coloration and fur patterns. All are characterized by long tails, cheek pouches and relatively simple digestive tracts that can handle a quite omnivorous diet. Guenons wander through the forest canopy in loosely organized troops, seldom with any particular individual in command. When the situation is peaceful, they keep up a steady conversation of self-satisfied grunts and croaks; when a dangerous predator threatens, however, they freeze in the highest branches and remain absolutely silent. They are almost entirely arboreal and have attained a high degree of finesse in tree-top locomotion. Their style, however, is markedly different from that of other monkeys: instead of leaping from one particular branch to another, they dash into space, aiming at the centre of a dense clump of foliage. When they land, they scramble through the small branches on to a large limb; from there, they hurl themselves towards their next objective. Even though this performance sometimes resembles a slapstick comedy, guenons can move through the trees as fast as a man can run on the ground.

OWL-FACED GUENON

HE GUENON KNOWN AS DE BRAZZA'S MONKEY IS EASILY IDENTIFIED BY THE DIGNIFIED GOATEE FOUND IN MATURE MALES.

THE GELADA BABOON lives high in the mountains of Ethiopia, usually making its home in rocky ravines. It can be distinguished from other baboons by its jutting lower jaw, rounded head and the heart-shaped patch of bare red skin on its chest.

OLD WORLD MONKEYS

The Powerful Ground Dwellers

Baboons and macaques, the most successful of the ground-dwelling monkeys, are strong creatures well equipped to stand their ground and fight off dangerous predators. They range from Africa to Japan, but nowhere do the two species overlap—convincing evidence that they are members of a single continuous radiation of monkeys. Further proof of this is found in their striking physiological and behavioural similarities. In fact, no other primate except man has ranged so far with so little change in physical structure. Hamadryad baboons (*opposite*) were among the most common animals in ancient Egypt and were revered as companions and oracles of the god Thoth. This status also gained for them the honour of being mummified at death.

A HAMADRYAD BABOON BARES ITS CANINES IN A TYPICAL THREAT POSTURE.

3

The Apes: Pioneers on Two Legs

"IT is almost impossible", the English naturalist William Charles Martin wrote of a female gibbon in 1840, "to convey in words an idea of the quickness and graceful address of her movements: they may indeed be termed aerial as she seems merely to touch in her progress the branches among which she exhibits her evolutions." No one since has suggested more vividly the sense of flowing, careless rhythm which makes a gibbon in the trees one of the most graceful spectacles nature has to offer. The gibbon is the arborealist supreme. It moves by swinging itself from branch to branch—or brachiating, as this movement is known—clutching briefly with alternate hands, before again hurling itself forward. The precision of its judgment is breathtaking; its dexterity is almost unbelievable. A gibbon can pluck a bird out of the air with one hand in the middle of a jump, then grasp the branch at which it is aiming with the other. C. R. Carpenter, who has devoted a lifetime to primate studies, once observed a branch break under a gibbon just as it launched itself into the air for a long leap. Turning in mid-air, it reached back, grasped the remaining stump, swung around it, over the top, and then, with almost no break in momentum, made the long outward jump of up to 30 feet to the next tree.

GIBBON

LIMBER FORELIMBS

One of the basic differences between apes and monkeys is in the greater freedom of movement that the former have in their forelimbs. Apes are brachiators; they can swing by their arms and move them freely in all directions (gibbon, above). Most monkeys, by contrast, are true quadrupeds. Since they travel on four limbs, they need only move their front legs forwards and backwards (macaque, below) and just a little bit to the side.

MACAQUE

The gibbon, as already stated, is an ape—a member of the family that also contains the orang-outang, the chimpanzee and the gorilla. This picture of the gibbon as a superlative acrobat flying through the tree-tops forms a sharp contrast to the popular conception of apes in general as large, clumsy, blundering creatures. But then apes, like monkeys, are infertile ground for generalization, and most attempts to categorize them run into difficulty. Take the question of how they are related to one another. One obvious way to answer it is to start with geography, putting the gibbon and orang-outang of Asia into one category, and the gorilla and chimpanzee of Africa into another. Such a distinction does have its points. Gibbons and orangs are predominantly arboreal; gorillas and chimpanzees are quite at home on the ground. Gibbons and orangs live in very small groups; the African apes in much larger ones. Yet the impression this distinction conveys is misleading. Taxonomically, gibbons are different enough from the other apes to be placed in a separate subfamily of their own. They stand only about three feet tall, and none weighs more than 25 pounds, far less than many monkeys. Unlike the other apes, they are apparently no more intelligent than monkeys. And in their agility and speed in the trees, they resemble arboreal monkeys far more closely than they resemble the gorilla or the orang.

Hurtling around just below the top canopy of densely clustered trees that reach more than a hundred feet high, gibbons are peculiarly difficult to study, and we know much less about them than we would like. We know about their anatomy. We know they live in small groups of a male and female together with their young. We know that both males and females are so jealous of members of the same sex that the young are forced by the hostility of one or the other of their parents to go off on their own as soon as they are sexually mature. We know that each separate group preserves its distance from intruders by issuing loud, warning hoots.

About orangs even less is known. Although they are fully as arboreal as gibbons, they are as slow and deliberate as gibbons are rapid and daring. Orangs possess some very curious characteristics, both in their physical make-up and in some of their movements. In the trees, they climb about with ease, using their hands and feet almost interchangeably and with astonishing flexibility. One of their remarkable positions is to hang from a branch by their feet, but with their bodies upright, their legs reaching up on either side above their heads, and their hands resting on their bellies. On the ground, they walk very awkwardly; although they go on all fours, their arms are much longer than their legs, and as a result their bodies are raised up as they move, giving them the look of an old man, bent by age and making his way with the aid of two sticks.

Or consider their faces. Orangs have a marvellous command of their facial muscles, especially around the mouth and nose. They can move parts of their big lips to produce a variety of expressions which would make any human television comedian envious. Presumably, these twitches are a form of communication. The cheeks of an adult male bulge out in fleshy lobes, unique among primates; below them, large air sacs connecting with the larynx can be blown up like enormous goitres. These sacs act as resonators, and orangs in the jungle have been heard to give enormously loud burps. Their purpose? Perhaps to serve as a warning signal. Finally, the males are about twice as large as the females. This is peculiar, since the accepted explanation for sexual dimorphism—that the males of ground-living species have become larger to defend the group against potential predators—clearly does not fit the arboreal orang.

Orangs once ranged over a much wider area than they now occupy. For there are today fewer than 5,000 of them still outside captivity, scattered across some 2,000 square miles of the dense Borneo forests and in the northern tip of Sumatra. They are continually hunted, usually for zoos. Unless some way can be found to stop the hunting, all the orangs not in captivity may soon disappear, and our curiosity about them will remain for ever unsatisfied.

Until very recently, the gorilla was practically as unknown a quantity as the orang still remains. What is worse, it was thoroughly misunderstood. Any man as maligned as the gorilla has been could have collected heavy damages for libel from all the travellers who have so reviled it in their memoirs. To zoologists and laymen alike, the gorilla has traditionally stood as the representative of man's primitive savagery unalleviated by the gentling influences of civilization. Killing for killing's sake, tearing limb from limb any innocent human unlucky enough to venture within range, gorillas were tailor-made to act the villain in horror films. Just as Rin Tin Tin was Everyman's dog, King Kong was his gorilla.

The misunderstanding was natural enough because nature, one might say, has cast the gorilla for the villain's role. It looks ferocious. A full-grown adult male stands about six feet tall and weighs more than 400 pounds, much of it in its mighty chest and massive arms, which suggest irresistibly the possibility of a deathly hug. Its face is, if anything, even more frightening, with huge teeth enclosed in a massive jaw and supported by a heavy ridge of bone around the skull. More than that, it beats its chest and pretends to charge when alarmed—a terrifying spectacle to anyone suddenly confronted by it. What the gorilla's appearance suggested, the travellers' tales confirmed. In 1856, the explorer Paul Du Chaillu ventured into the dark and cavernous forests which stretch inland from the West African coast and house what is now called the lowland gorilla. Du Chaillu was actually a perceptive observer but, like other explorers, he tended to shoot first when he came across a gorilla and do his observing later. His report that the gorilla reminded him of "some hellish dream creature—a being of that hideous order, half-man half-beast", lent support to the equally terrifying accounts given by the Africans. When in 1892 another explorer, R. L. Garner, ventured into the West African jungle to study gorillas and chimpanzees, he thoughtfully built himself an iron cage to sit in so that the gorillas could not get at him. Waiting for the animals to come to him, Garner found out very little about lowland gorillas, and though many have since been hunted and shot, the dense, dark jungle has discouraged even the most dedicated zoologists from carrying out a close and continued study of the species.

ABOUT a thousand miles to the east, in the eastern Congo and western Uganda, another thick, tropical forest encircles the slopes of two mountain massifs. This forest is the home of the mountain gorilla. Today some 5,000 to 15,000 gorillas live there, in danger of extinction and forced to retreat steadily farther up the mountain side as the lower slopes are occupied by man and turned over to his cattle.

This is the area where, early in 1959, the distribution of the mountain gorilla was surveyed by two zoologists from the University of Wisconsin, John Emlen and George Schaller. Emlen returned home after six months, but Schaller, accompanied by his wife, established himself on the mountain slopes of the Albert National Park and stayed on until September 1960. For much of the time, the two lived in a small hut in a meadow near the forest where each day Schaller ventured out to follow and observe the gorillas. He has described what he found

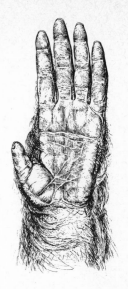

HAND OF ORANG-OUTANG

LONG, HOOKING FINGERS

The most arboreal of the apes, the brachiating gibbons and orang-outangs, have specialized hands with extraordinarily long, strong fingers that can be flexed into hooks for hanging and swinging. Their thumbs, however, are different. That of the orang is short and stumpy and does not get in the way during brachiation. The gibbon's is longer, and although sometimes used in climbing, can be neatly tucked alongside the palm when its owner is using its other fingers to travel by swinging from branch to branch.

HAND OF GIBBON

in two magnificent books, *The Mountain Gorilla* and *The Year of the Gorilla.* They contain practically everything that is known about gorillas in the wild; all the statements in this book about gorillas in their natural habitat have been drawn from them.

Unlike his predecessors, Schaller approached the gorillas without his finger itching on a trigger, and he discovered that, far from being the ferocious beasts of legend, gorillas are actually mild-mannered vegetarians who like to mind their own business. They were at first startled by Schaller's intrusion. Usually when he appeared, an adult male would rise and give a roar of alarm or beat his chest threateningly at Schaller before fading into the trees after the females and the young. But once they realized he was not dangerous, curiosity replaced fear. While Schaller observed them, they observed him: the young gorillas with open interest, the adults more covertly, like suburban wives peering through the curtains, as if embarrassed to let him see they cared. Occasionally Schaller blundered into a gorilla emerging from the trees. Having already noticed that some of the individuals he had been studying would shake their heads almost in an appeasing way—as if to relieve embarrassment—when he stared at them too fixedly, he decided to try the same thing in the tense moment of a sudden, too-close confrontation. So, whenever he did accidentally come face to face with a male gorilla, Schaller would shake his head vigorously, whereupon the gorilla would turn and move off back into the forest.

A CTUALLY gorillas have little reason to be ferocious. While their ancestors were probably in danger from predators when they first descended from the trees, today's males are so large and powerful that a group is never attacked except, very rarely, by a leopard turned gorilla hunter. Because they need enormous quantities of food, the adults spend from six to eight hours a day eating, and much of their bulk is due to their large digestive tract.

Its sheer size and bulk make climbing trees an awkward business for an adult, especially a full-grown male. While the young gorillas nip around with ease in the trees, the adults climb with caution. Even so, branches do break under their weight and they may fall several feet before gaining a fresh, secure hold. Actually the adults spend about four-fifths of their time on the ground and they ascend trees only for some specific purpose: to eat, to obtain a longer view or to sleep. Like orangs and chimpanzees, they build nests to sleep in, but while chimpanzees may sleep 100 feet up in the trees, gorilla nests, if built in trees, are rarely more than 10 feet up.

When building a nest in a tree, a gorilla picks a firm site in a fork or along a stout branch and then bends or weaves in adjacent branches and vines to form a secure platform. Chimpanzees and orangs normally refine the technique by adding a final layer of leafy branchlets to make their nests more comfortable. The reason why the great apes build nests in trees is obvious: they are too big simply to balance all night in a fork or on a branch without serious danger of falling out. As nest builders they are also gradually losing the toughened skin pads on their rumps—possessed by all Old World monkeys, which characteristically sleep sitting on branches. Gibbons do not build nests and have retained the skin pads. However, only about a third of chimpanzees have them, and even fewer orangs and gorillas. A behavioural adaptation, in other words, has replaced a biological one: the nest has replaced the rump pads.

The gorilla's sleeping habits are very curious. Other primates sleep in trees to avoid predators, but gorillas are not afraid of predators and they often sleep

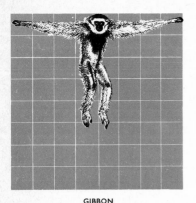

GIBBON

LONG LIMBS FOR TRAVEL

The more a primate depends on a single pair of limbs for locomotion, the longer and stronger these limbs become, as is shown in these two drawings. The gibbon, enlarged here for comparison with man, travels from branch to branch by swinging from its arms which have become so elongated that their span easily exceeds the total length of its body and legs. Man, by contrast, having developed the ability to walk upright, has long legs. His arm span, unlike that of the gibbon, is no greater than his height.

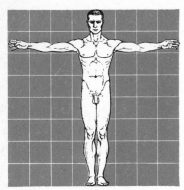

MAN

on the ground. Their tree-sleeping proclivities are presumably vestigial—a relic from earlier times when they had to build arboreal nests for their own protection. The same may be said of the way they still build nests on the ground. Under some circumstances, these seem to be quite useless—scarcely nests at all. For example, they are often located on a slope so that the occupant rolls out during the night and wakes up in the morning several feet away. This illustrates how a habit like nest building may be maintained by a species even though it is only useful in certain locations.

With nothing to fear—except man—and plenty of food available, the gorillas Schaller encountered lived in a state of mild and amiable serenity. Most of them lived in groups of 6 to 17, each one led by a powerful silver-back male, so called from the saddle of grizzled silver hairs which begin to sprout up among the black ones when a male gorilla reaches the age of 10. His dominance over the group is absolute, but normally genial. Occasionally a young gorilla will get too frolicsome and be silenced by a glare or a threatening slap on the ground from an adult. Sometimes a couple of females will begin to scream at each other until the leader glares at them and they promptly calm down. The leader, however, is no stern paterfamilias. When he wants quiet, he gets quiet, but except for one or two particularly irascible silver-backs, the leaders are usually quite approachable. Females nestle against them and infants crawl happily over their huge bodies. Amity reigns. When a band of gorillas is at rest, the young play, the mothers tend their infants, and the other adults lie at peace and soak up the sun.

In his book *No Room in the Ark*, the Australian writer Alan Moorehead gives a dramatic description of his first encounter with a free mountain gorilla. He had been climbing all day in the Kirunga range of Central Africa and was thoroughly tired when at last his guides sighted a gorilla. "I looked at the point where they were staring", he writes, "and I remember calling out aloud, 'Oh my God, how wonderful!'

"AND the truth is he was wonderful. He was a huge shining male, half crouching, half standing, his mighty arms akimbo. I had not been prepared for the blackness of him; he was a great craggy pillar of gleaming blackness, black crew-cut hair on his head, black deep-sunken eyes glaring towards us, huge rubbery black nostrils and a black beard. He shifted his posture a little, still glaring fixedly upon us, and he had the dignity and majesty of prophets. He was the most distinguished and splendid animal I ever saw and I had only one desire at that moment: to go forward towards him, to meet him and to know him: to communicate . . . with the gorilla there is an instant sense of recognition. You might be badly frightened, but in the end you feel you will be able to make some gesture, utter some sound, that the animal will recognize and understand."

Schaller, as day by day he got to know them better, was more and more impressed by the gorillas' resemblance to humans. Like men, they yawn and stretch when they awake in the morning, and sit, dangling their legs over the sides of their nests. They pick their noses, scratch themselves when puzzled and, if nervous or excited, they often begin to eat vigorously, much as a man might pull at a cigarette. That they experience human emotions—annoyance and uneasiness, curiosity and boldness—Schaller has no doubt. Though there is great individual variation of temperament among gorillas, there is about them a curious reserve, as if they are reluctant to show their feelings. It is al-

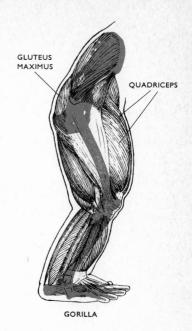

GLUTEUS MAXIMUS

QUADRICEPS

GORILLA

WHY MAN WALKS BETTER

Why can't a gorilla walk and stand like a man? Because of differences in leg bone and muscle. Man has a strongly developed buttock muscle, the gluteus maximus, which pulls his body forward and over his leg with each stride. In the gorilla, the gluteus maximus is relatively underdeveloped, so the best it can do bipedally is a shuffle. But man also has the ability to lock his legs at the knee so that when he is standing erect he does not need to use his quadriceps to hold himself up. The gorilla, unable to lock its legs, can stand up only in a tiring crouch.

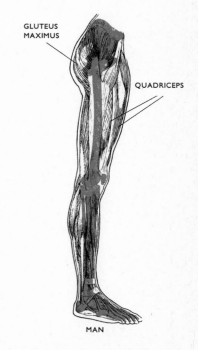

GLUTEUS MAXIMUS

QUADRICEPS

MAN

most as if they were shy, unwilling to reveal themselves to the inspection of the curious, or perhaps so self-assured that they disdain to show their emotions, out of indifference to the opinion of others.

None the less, gorillas can exhibit strong feelings, especially when they feel threatened. They scream in alarm and as a warning to other members of the group. They toss leaves in the air. They also beat their chests. All gorillas, even the very young ones, do this, rising up on two legs on the ground, or popping up amid the foliage of a tree to give a few brief slaps before fading out of sight. The full performance, however, is put on only by the silver-back males, and it is as formalized as the entrance of a fighter into the boxing ring. It begins inconspicuously with a series of soft, clear hoots which gradually quicken. Already, the silver-back apparently expects to command attention because, if interrupted, he is liable to look around in annoyance. As he continues to hoot, he may stop, pluck a leaf from a plant near by and place it between his lips. This curiously incongruous and delicate gesture is a prelude to coming violence and, when they see it, the other gorillas get out of his way. The violence is not immediate. First the gorilla rises to his full height and slaps his hands on his chest or his belly, on his thigh or on another gorilla, producing a booming sound that can be heard a mile away. The chest beating over, the violence erupts. He runs sideways for a few steps, then he drops down on all fours and breaks into a full-speed dash, wrenching branches from trees and slapping violently at everything in his way, including any other members of the group who do not have the wit to keep clear. Finally, there comes the last gesture: the silver-back thumps the palm of his hand violently on the ground, and then sits back, looking as if he is now ready to hear the applause.

T HE chest-beating display seems to serve a variety of purposes. It may be self-assertion, threat, challenge—or all three rolled into one. And probably it originated as a form of displacement activity, an action performed when an animal is torn by conflicting emotions and avoids decision by doing something quite irrelevant, as a man may beat the table instead of hitting his boss. But from this simple beginning it has entered now into a highly complex and ritualized form of bluff. Although his practice of beating his chest has contributed to the gorilla's reputation for fearsomeness, it is not so much an act of aggression as a substitute for it. An angry gorilla may bluff and threaten another gorilla but he rarely fights. Schaller describes one incident which illustrates the point to perfection. Normally, two strange groups of gorillas will pass each other, and even intermingle, without any signs of hostility. But once, when two such groups came together, one leader apparently felt that his position was threatened and he tried to assert it by cowing the leader of the other group. Several times he rushed at his rival, stopping only an inch away with his head thrust forward, trying to stare the other silver-back down. His supreme effort was to throw a handful of leaves in the air in a gesture of challenge. But when the other male refused to be intimidated, the silver-back gave up his attempts and retreated. His actions were actually intended to avoid a fight, but from evidence of several tufts of hair pulled out by the roots and found on the trail the following day, Schaller concluded that "a tussle probably occurred".

Almost inevitably, one finds oneself comparing the gorilla to his fellow African ape, the chimpanzee. It is an intriguing exercise and full of paradoxes. At first glance, they look physically very different. A full-grown chimpanzee male is much smaller than a male gorilla, 10 to 12 inches less in height and

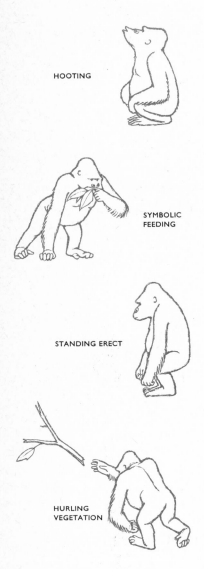

A GORILLA'S EMOTIONAL DISPLAY

The famous chest-beating display of a mountain gorilla is actually just one phase in an elaborate ritual giving vent to anger, fear, or mere annoyance. As shown here, it begins with hooting and continues with increasing excitement to a climactic thumping of the ground. A display by one male may start an entire group on a chest-beating spree. Infants at play may perform parts of the ritual, and sometimes adults do a little languid chest beating while lolling on the ground.

HOOTING

SYMBOLIC FEEDING

STANDING ERECT

HURLING VEGETATION

barely a third the weight. And apart from his smaller stature, the chimpanzee looks altogether less ferocious. He possesses neither the gorilla's huge teeth nor his massive facial musculature. None the less, the two apes are anatomically very similar. What distinguishes them most clearly is their diet, their behaviour and their temperament.

Gorillas eat mostly ground plants. Chimpanzees feed mostly on fruit, and they are predominantly arboreal. They travel on the ground as easily as gorillas and in much the same manner, supporting their weight on the soles of their feet and on toughened skin pads below their knuckles. Still, they spend some three-quarters of their time in the trees; they are much more arboreal than gorillas but less so than orangs. And where orangs are slow and deliberate, chimpanzees are often fast and impulsive, climbing around a hundred feet above the ground with the ease of a monkey.

CHEST
BEATING

LEG
KICKING

RUNNING
SIDEWAYS

UPROOTING
VEGETATION

GROUND
THUMPING

Like most monkeys which live in trees, chimpanzees are noisy. They seem to love noise for its own sake, and very little is needed to provoke them into a chorus of hoots and high-pitched screams which transform the forest into bedlam. They may hoot when they come across a rich supply of fruit, when they wake up and when they make their nests at night, and when two groups meet or a large group breaks up. Frequently their calls are backed up with a great stamping in the trees, a shaking of branches and a reverberating drum roll produced by pounding on the buttresses of ironwood trees.

Africans have told of "carnivals" that last for hours, the noise rising to a crescendo in one part of the forest after another. Chimpanzees seem especially sensitive to the intrusions of humans. Frequently, they greet visitors with a few opening hoots, then, after a few moments of quiet, they start up again, but this time at full volume, complete with shrieks and hoots and drum rolls. Strangers to the forest have admitted being terrified by the sudden stunning uproar which is rendered all the more frightening by the fact that the noise-makers remain invisible, concealed high in the forest canopy. Chimpanzees can be very dangerous, but if given a choice they will flee from man in the wild. From the safety of a tree, they will brandish branches they have torn off, a behaviour also practised by orangs and several kinds of monkeys. Probably chimpanzees screech and shake branches for much the same reasons that gorillas throw leaves in the air or beat their chests: not so much to inflict actual damage but as a form of defiance or challenge, or out of anger.

Most of our information about chimpanzees in the wild comes from a husband-wife team, Vernon and Frances Reynolds, who studied chimpanzees in the Endongo Forest, Uganda, and from Jane Goodall, who is still studying them in Northern Tanzania. After leaving secondary school in England, Miss Goodall took a job in East Africa as secretary to the distinguished prehistorian Louis Leakey. Noticing that she showed real promise as a field research worker, Leakey promised to give her a chance to study chimpanzees in the wild if she would get some university training. She worked under primatologists in England for a year, and later was established on a field station in a remote part of Tanzania. Her principal research weapons were an intense determination and a deep affection for chimpanzees. There were between 100 and 200 of these animals in the Gombe Stream Chimpanzee Reserve where Miss Goodall launched her study—all of them wild, afraid of humans and as anxious to keep away from her as she was to get close to them. It took her about 14 months of patient, persistent daily tracking before she could approach to within 30 or 40 feet of them without disturbing their normal activities. Ultimately she broke down their fear of her entirely and became accepted as one of the group—thus she was able, for instance, to pick burrs from the hair of certain animals, a service which they reciprocated.

Miss Goodall has witnessed one of the most puzzling chimpanzee displays, a performance she has entitled the "rain dance". Describing one such occasion, she tells how she was watching a group of chimpanzees in a tree half-way up the side of a steep valley. When rain started falling, the chimpanzees came down from the tree and started walking up the grassy slope in two groups. At the sky-line, the females and juveniles climbed high into the trees. Then, as the rain turned into a violent tropical deluge, the males, amid crashes of thunder, began their spectacular display. One, turning suddenly, charged diagonally down the slope, slapping the ground as it went, and as though this were a signal, all the other males joined in. Some charged down hitting at vegetation, others sprang into the trees, tore off great branches, hurled themselves to the ground and raced down the hill-side at breakneck speed dragging the branches behind them. At the bottom, each chimpanzee swung up into a tree to break its headlong flight. There it sat for a moment before climbing down and plodding up the hill again to resume, with wild cries, its downward rush. Then, as suddenly as it began, the show was over; the spectators climbed down from the trees and the whole group disappeared over the horizon.

WHAT provokes the chimpanzees to put on such a performance? Possibly it is an expression of irritation at the rain. Possibly it is also a form of sexual display. The males exhibit their strength and prowess, and the females, one trusts, are properly impressed. But—and this again is only suggestion—there may be more involved than mere irritation or sexual braggadocio. Activities like football and dancing, including even chimpanzee "dancing", are expressions of exuberance practised most vigorously by extroverts—and extroversion is always tinged with the hues of exhibitionism. Chimpanzees are the extroverts among the apes, and the most unabashedly exhibitionistic. They revel in applause; they love attention. They shine at the tea parties which are a traditional form of entertainment in some zoos. Indeed, chimpanzees give the impression that they positively look forward to displaying their table manners, unlike gorillas or orangs who are acutely uncomfortable at such affairs.

Any animal that wants an audience must be ready to please it. So, as one might expect, chimpanzees are the most compliant of the apes. That is to say, young chimpanzees; old ones, especially old males, often become thoroughly intractable and even dangerous in captivity. But young chimpanzees do very well in laboratory intelligence tests, both because they are intelligent and because they are willing to oblige their masters. One could fill pages with examples. Chimpanzees have learned to ride bicycles, smoke cigarettes and put on evening dress. As a publicity stunt, they have been trained to work on assembly lines, stuffing foam rubber into pillows and putting full-sized beds into cartons. They can drive tractors and they can steer motor-cars, and, in fact, they can do the latter in so human a manner that, in December of 1963, a Florida police patrol picked up a chimpanzee for speeding.

Actually, he was only steering. His owner, a carnival showman, was operating the pedals. Still, it would be hard to imagine a gorilla steering a car or driving a tractor, or performing on television. This is not because a gorilla lacks the intellectual capacity to perform such feats. His brain, so far as we can tell, is as developed as a chimpanzee's. But how far can we tell? Professor Robert M. Yerkes, one of the founding fathers of primatology, who carried out many classic studies of captive apes, came to the conclusion that his test gorilla, a young female, was slow at intelligence tests because she was timid and introverted, and lacked the chimpanzees' interest in winning her keepers' good opinions. Being reserved and self-sufficient, gorillas just may not be prepared to perform the kind of tests that humans devise to satisfy human curiosity.

There is another reason why laboratory tests, unless they are really sophisticated and well planned, can be misleading in the conclusions they suggest about the intelligence of non-human primates. All too often in the past, they tested abilities that might have seemed important to humans but did not happen to be at all important to monkeys or apes. Suppose a Londoner were to be trapped by a group of chimpanzees, shipped to Africa and stuck up in a tree a hundred feet above the ground. Practically all his abilities—his mastery of language, his skill at fixing a disabled fuel pump, his aggressive salesmanship —would be irrelevant to his situation. Hanging on for dear life, frequently confusing edible with poisonous plants and, no doubt, experiencing grave difficulties in distinguishing one chimpanzee from another, he would appear to his captors to be an exceedingly stupid animal. Their judgment, of course, would be unfair, since it would arise from a failure to appreciate that Londoners are not used to living in trees.

Odd as it may appear, many of the early laboratory psychologists who first began to try to appraise the intelligence of monkeys and apes fell into precisely this kind of error. Take, for example, the famous box-stacking test. A chimpanzee, say, is placed in a cage where a banana is hanging a few feet above his reach. The only way he can get it is by stacking up the boxes that have been left scattered around the cage. If he stacks three boxes on top of one another and then climbs up and grabs hold of the banana, he is given a certain rating. Then the banana is placed higher. If the chimpanzee can then stack four boxes and get the banana, he is rated very highly. If, on the other hand, he commits the blunder of dragging out the bottom box to put on top of the others, so that the whole pile collapses, he is considered to have failed.

Then there is the food-and-sticks test. A monkey is chained to a spot a few feet away from a food reward, with a short stick left lying within his reach, and another, longer stick just beyond it. His task is to use the short stick to draw in the long stick, and then to use the long stick to draw in the food. The quicker he learns to do it, the brighter he is judged to be.

THE trouble with these tests is that they actually tell us almost nothing about the intelligence of monkeys and apes because they are conducted with objects and in situations which are abnormal to the animal concerned. Monkeys are not adapted to manipulating objects; chimpanzees do not encounter boxes in the wild which they can stack to bring an inaccessible banana within reach. Yet in the wild both monkeys and chimpanzees—or all apes, for that matter—can be extremely intelligent in learning the things that matter to them: obtaining food, avoiding or overcoming enemies and, in the case of many species, getting along with the group—a truly significant ability which had not been tested in laboratory experiments at all.

Actually, the chimpanzee is a very gifted animal, not much inferior in intelligence, one might guess, to the ape-like ancestors from which the first bipedal men emerged. A young chimpanzee is as intelligent as a human child before the child learns to talk. Like children, young chimpanzees are also extremely inquisitive, and in captivity they will work diligently at a problem, apparently for the pure satisfaction of solving it. Chimpanzees, like all the other apes and monkeys, even learn to control their emotions. In the wild, a young chimpanzee learns as it matures not to irritate the adults. As a juvenile, it learns to control its natural exuberance in play with infants of the group so as to avoid injuring them. In fact, so far as control of the emotions is concerned, the principal difference between an adult monkey or ape and an adult human being is one of degree: contrary to Freud, repression of emotions is by no means a monopoly of man.

The fact of the matter is that intelligence is not a single thing. What is really important is an animal's ability to learn. What has evolved in animals is the ability to learn those things which are of importance to them, and to survival of the species. In the course of evolution, furthermore, certain abilities have decreased while others have increased in efficiency. A blindfolded man, relying on his sense of smell alone, would fail at making many distinctions which would be easy for a lemur. The lemur, testing human intelligence, might mark out a scent trail through the branches of a tree, only to discover that "moron man" could not follow the trail at all. In the same way, chimpanzees are different from men in their ability to use tools and language. Their ability to use tools is very limited, and though great efforts have been made to teach them to talk, they can learn the meaning of only a very few words and cannot enunciate any.

INTELLIGENCE, then, is not something general but a series of specific abilities to learn and perform. This is what the far more sophisticated tests of today are aimed at—and not in comparison to human standards, either, but in comparisons of one animal species to another. And by these standards—the relative learning abilities of a lemur, a rhesus monkey and a chimpanzee—we can get some measure of the progressive advancement of species from the primitive to the advanced types.

What the field studies of recent times have contributed to our understanding of intelligence among apes and monkeys is an awareness of the rich and complicated lives which these creatures normally learn to live. They learn to distinguish many different kinds of food plants, they learn all the intricacies of a complex and variegated range, they learn the problems of predators, the social hierarchy and the way of life of the troop. And from troop to troop this whole complex of behaviour varies not only according to the biology of the species but also according to the history of the troop concerned.

We are prone to think of apes and monkeys as creatures without the power of conceptual thought—and this may be true, though again it may also be just a question of degree. We know they have the ability to plan—can we say they do not reflect upon the past and the future? Certainly they learn from the past. And if we think of them as concerned only with their immediate needs— obtaining food, avoiding danger, getting along with their fellows, raising their young; in short, living only in the present—is this not largely true of humans too? Professor Adriaan Kortlandt has described how he once watched a chimpanzee gazing at a sunset for a full 15 minutes, sitting quietly and watching the changing colours until the western sky grew dark. Anthropomorphic romanticizing? Perhaps. Yet surely it would be very arrogant of man to assume without question that only he can experience the sensation of awe or find pleasure in the beauty of an African twilight.

THOUGH IT IS ESSENTIALLY A QUADRUPED, A CHIMPANZEE CAN AND DOES WALK UPRIGHT. ALOFT, IT CAN BE NEARLY AS AGILE AS A GIBBON.

The Anthropoids

Man's closest relatives are the apes—gibbons, chimpanzees, gorillas and orang-outangs. They vary greatly in appearance and behaviour, from feather-weight gibbons that spend their lives in the branches to massive gorillas that are most at home on the ground. But these expressive, intelligent creatures have many anatomical and behavioural features that link them to each other—and to man.

THIS MULTIPLE PHOTOGRAPH SHOWS A BRACHIATING GIBBON IN PERFECT FORM. RELEASING ONE HAND, IT SWINGS SWIFTLY FORWARDS AND GRA

A Swinging Primate

The ability to brachiate, or swing hand over hand through the trees, is a characteristic of the apes, although not all of them make frequent use of it. The undisputed king of the art is the gibbon, whose slight body, elongated arms and fingers make it beautifully suited to arboreal locomotion. The gibbon's wrist, arm and shoulder are especially adapted for mobility as it reaches, grasps and changes its holds; proportionately, its arms are longer than those of any other ape. When a gibbon is peacefully brachiating along, it usually travels at about the speed of the average human walk. But when it is excited or frightened, it can plunge through the forest canopy at astonishing speeds, sometimes cov-

72

E ROPE AHEAD OF ITS OTHER HAND, THEN REPEATS THE PROCESS IN A SERIES OF FLUID ACTIONS RESULTING IN CONTINUOUS FORWARD MOVEMENT.

ering 30 feet or more in a single jump without a break in its "stride". With each leap gravity carries it closer to the ground; after two or three leaps, it clambers high into the branches again for a fresh series of leaps. Although great bursts of high-speed brachiation are short-lived, they are quite sufficient to put hundreds of yards between a gibbon and its most serious predator, the leopard. On rare occasions, a gibbon has been seen to seize a long vine and swing Tarzan-like to another tree. Even if a gibbon is surprised by a predator on open ground, it can usually flee to safety, running on two feet like a man, but holding its arms up at a dainty angle for balance and to keep them from dragging on the ground.

73

CLUTCHING HER INFANT PROTECTIVELY, A GIBBON SHOWS THE INTENSE MATERNAL CARE LAVISHED ON THE YOUNG UNTIL THEY ARE WEANED.

At Home with the Gibbons

Why has the gibbon alone remained small and agile when the rest of the apes have evolved towards ever-increasing size? One answer is that, for their specialized way of life, natural selection favoured the smaller individuals: the gibbon's light weight and agility ensure it virtual freedom from predators and a limitless food supply. The greatest portion of its diet is made up of fruit—figs, mangoes, grapes and plums. Sometimes, as though for a treat, a gibbon will steal a bird's nest and carry it cafeteria-fashion

to a comfortable perch, where it will devour the eggs. At night the gibbon sits or curls up on its side in the branches to sleep—it is the only one of the apes that does not build nests. At birth, a gibbon is just about as helpless as its human counterpart, but in a few weeks it awakens to the world around it: it smells flowers, plays with its feet and eagerly tastes anything it can get into its mouth. By the time it is about a year old it has an established social life revolving around its parents and siblings.

ONLY A GIBBON WOULD EVER WALK A VINE LIKE THIS; EVEN THE NIMBLEST MONKEYS WOULD USE ALL FOURS

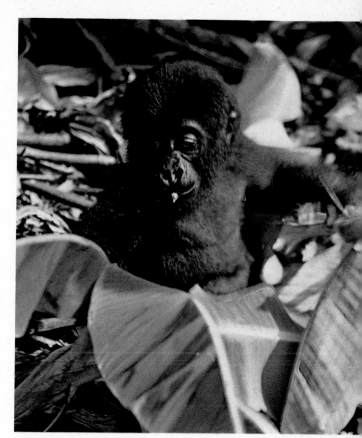

A BABY GORILLA chews tentatively on a tender shoot. Its elders are always nearby, ready to defend the baby if necessary from any predator rash enough to attack.

The Gentle Giants

Despite all the atrocities falsely attributed to it, the gorilla is essentially a peace-loving creature that would rather retreat than fight except in circumstances when its life is threatened and retreat is impossible. In the wild it has never been seen eating meat, although individuals have learned to do so in captivity. Nor do gorillas seem to drink water in the wild; they apparently get what moisture they need from their diet of greenery and fruit. Their gentle nature is evident at an early age: at play, the juvenile gorillas are markedly solicitous of the often turbulent infants. Females mature at about seven and males at about ten years of age. Females have only one infant at a time and usually about one every three years.

THE GROUP RELAXES after a morning devoted to eating. A few groups may contain as many as 30 gorillas, but the majority are about a dozen.

A FUTILE NEST shows the power of instinct in a captive female gorilla. Although she may have a goal in mind, the pathetic pile of leaves that she finally accumulates serves no apparent purpose, any more than the rather useless nests gorillas build on the ground in the wild—probably relics from times when they were largely arboreal and built nests in the trees.

ERCELY MATERNAL, A FEMALE GORILLA CLASPS HER TINY INFANT IN HER ARMS AS SHE GLARES AT THE INTRUDING CAMERA.

THIS BEARDED MALE ORANG-OUTANG'S PENSIVE EXPRESSION CLEARLY SHOWS WHY NATIVES OF BORNEO CALL IT "THE MAN OF THE FOREST".

The Solitary Orang

Science knows less about orang-outangs than about any of the other apes. Their remote jungle habitat and their extreme shyness have precluded any thorough investigation of orang-outang behaviour except in unnatural conditions of captivity. But even in the wild the abiding impression of observers is summed up in such adjectives as "morose", "melancholy", "lethargic". Though admirably equipped for ar-

boreal locomotion, orangs usually proceed through the trees at a deliberate pace, seldom releasing more than one hand or foot at a time; they appear to move quickly only in times of extreme danger. Yet in their youth, orangs are active and playful, like other young apes: why they tend to become solitary as they mature will remain a mystery until they are studied much more extensively in the wild.

81

AN ORANG CLIMBS WITH CHARACTERISTIC CAUTION, HANGING ON WITH HANDS AND FEET WHILE IT HUNTS FOR FRUIT.

Skeletons from Monkey to Man

Because of their separate evolutionary development over the past millions of years, monkeys, apes and men have today a variety of skeletal forms which, in part, reflect their different modes of locomotion. The monkeys are slender with slim hips, compressed rib cages and the longest spinal column, ideally flexible for rapid climbing and leaping. The apes are basically constructed as brachiators, even though the gorilla shown here spends nearly all its time on the ground. They have long, powerful arms with hook-like hands adapted for grasping overhead limbs, and their shoulder blades and arm sockets are positioned and designed to allow for a wide range of arm movement above their heads. Their backs are almost inflexible—an adaptation that reflects their ability to hang by their arms. Man possesses a moderately flexible spinal column and has developed long legs for walking bipedally.

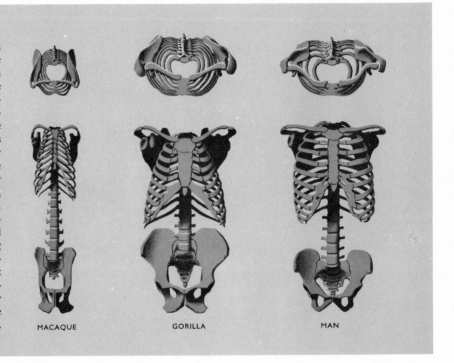

THREE PROFOUND CHANGES in structure from monkey to man are in the shoulder, the lumbar region of the spine and the pelvis. The monkey's shoulder blades are nearly parallel to each other on opposite sides of its rib cage; man's are on his upper back, and a gorilla's extend upwards with a great bony collar. Lumbar vertebrae—those with no ribs attached—usually number six or seven in monkeys, but most apes have only three. Man normally has five. In its quadrupedal stance, a monkey's tilted pelvis provides an anchor for its leg muscles. The gorilla's pelvis provides a base for muscles to support its heavy, stooped torso. Man's pelvis not only supports the upper body but is an excellent base for the powerful muscles used in walking.

MACAQUE   GORILLA   MAN

COMPARATIVE SKELETONS from a macaque monkey, gorilla and man illustrate the physiological progression from four-footedness to arm-swinging to two-legged walking. The monkey's arms are somewhat shorter than its legs; it can walk with its hands palms down, an impossible feat for a gorilla. On the other hand, the monkey's down-turned shoulder sockets prohibit brachiation in the true sense of the word. Man is less specialized and thus more adaptable: as an infant he can crawl palms down; as a youth he can brachiate—if clumsily—and he stands on two legs.

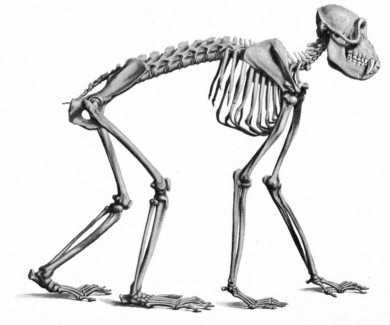

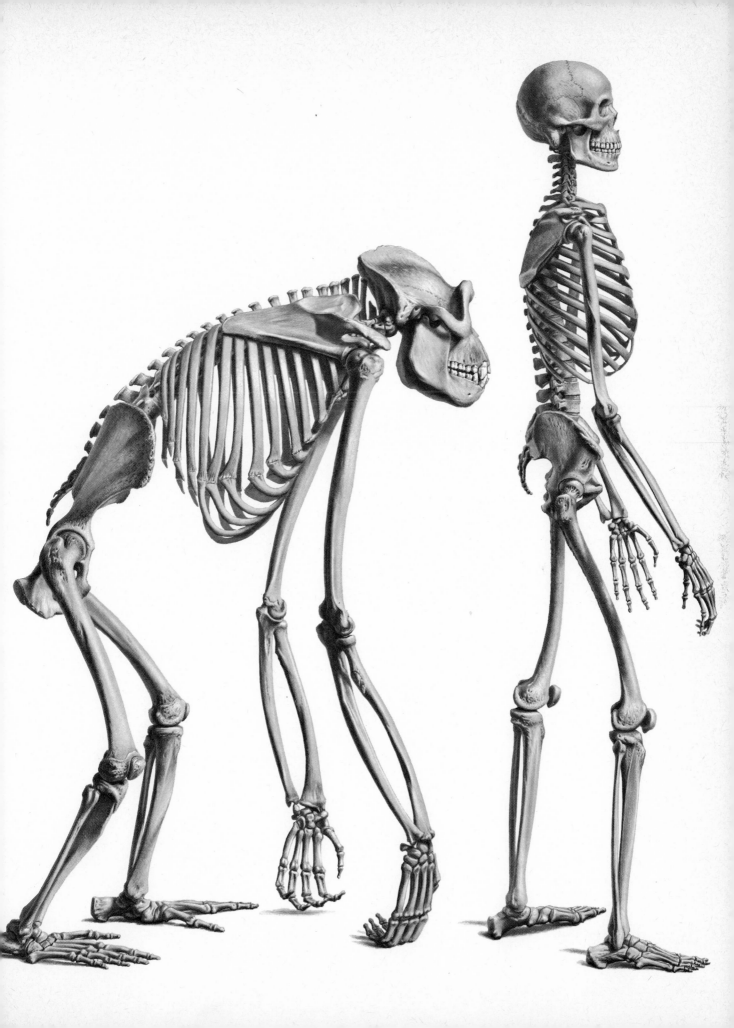

4

The Rewards
of Childhood

ANY event that happens with sufficient regularity is accepted by us as a matter of course. That is why we never question the normal human practice
of bearing one infant at a time. With us it is twins that are the surprise. Triplets are an astonishment, quadruplets command headlines, and quintuplets
make their parents' fortunes. Yet multiple birth is common among mammals,
with the multiplication sometimes running to two dozen or more babies at
a time. Why, then, does a human female have twins in only one out of 90 pregnancies, triplets in one out of 8,000, quads in one out of 700,000, quins in one
out of over 65 million? To ask the question more pointedly, why do human
females experience multiple births almost as rarely as monkeys and apes?

The form of the latter question supports the answer. There is much of the
monkey inside us still. Unlike many prosimians and marmosets, most monkeys
came to bear their young singly as a part of their adaptation to life in the trees.
It is not possible to say precisely why or when they acquired their birth pattern
or the particular kind of relationship which exists between a monkey female
and her new-born infant. But one can say that both the pattern and the relationship were acquired at least partly as a solution to the problem of transportation.

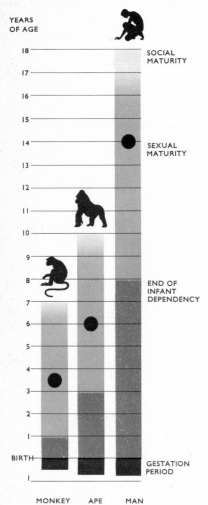

YEARS
OF AGE

18 — SOCIAL
MATURITY
17 —
16 —
15 —
14 — SEXUAL
MATURITY
13 —
12 —
11 —
10 —
9 —
8 — END OF
INFANT
DEPENDENCY
7 —
6 —
5 —
4 —
3 —
2 —
1 —
BIRTH
GESTATION
PERIOD
1 —

MONKEY   APE   MAN

LIVE AND LEARN

Compared to other animals, the primates grow up very slowly. This is because they have much to learn and need a long childhood in which to absorb it. The one that needs to learn the most (man) has the longest childhood of all. This chart shows how long a guenon monkey, a gorilla and a man stay in the womb and at what age each first achieves token independence of mother, then sexual maturity and, finally, social maturity as an adult. These stages are shown by different colour tones in the graph; lightening tone indicates increasing age and independence.

Throughout the day, monkeys are continually on the move from one feeding area to another, and the mother of a new-born infant is able to move quite freely and comfortably, using all four limbs, only because she has a single infant and because that infant clings to her hair; either to her front or, as in the case of some South American species, to her back.

To infant monkeys and apes, an effective grasp is almost as vital as breathing. They have to cling to mothers who are likely at any moment to perform some violent feat of acrobatics, either to escape from sudden danger or in the normal course of feeding. A gibbon, for example, even with a new-born infant clinging to her, remains an extraordinarily agile animal. She will feed at the end of a long branch, swaying perhaps in a high wind. Suddenly she will drop to another branch, run along it, and then start to swing again in the long, characteristic gibbon leaps, spanning perhaps 20 feet at a time. The infant cannot afford to relax its grip on her hair for a second because if it does and it is shaken loose, it is a dead gibbon.

WHAT impels it to grip so firmly? It is not enough to dismiss the infant's tenacious grasp as due simply to an instinct necessary for survival. To do so is to misunderstand the forces which provoke apes—or monkeys or men —to action. People do not eat because they need food to survive, nor do they practice sex because copulation is essential for the preservation of the species. Nor does a human mother hold and fondle her infant because if deprived of her attentions it would die. We eat, we copulate and, if we are mothers, we look after our babies, because such activities are pleasurable—which is simply another way of saying they satisfy a need.

So it is with infant monkeys. While the simple act of clinging may not seem very rewarding, it happens to give infant monkeys an enormous amount of gratification. Emotionally, they prefer an object to which they can cling, to one they can suck on. And if the reader is surprised, he will find himself in much the same frame of mind as did Professor Harry Harlow of the University of Wisconsin, when he made the discovery as a result of his well-known series of experiments with infant rhesus macaques and two simple types of dummy mothers. These were cylinder-shaped objects made of wire mesh and equipped with wooden heads and artificial breasts. Harlow named them "surrogate", or artificial, "mothers". Half of these dummies he left with their wire bodies bare, the others he covered with terry cloth. Then he set up a number of cages with a pair of dummy mothers accessible to each. For half of the cages he connected the "breasts" of the wire dummy with a milk supply, for the other half the terry cloth mother was the one who had the milk. Finally he put a new-born baby rhesus macaque into each cage and sat back to see what would happen.

There were several things the babies might have done. They might have ignored the dummy mothers altogether, only going to them to feed. Or they might have developed a special attachment to the dummy whose breast they fed from and remained near it between their meals. This presumably is what they would have done if suckling were the strongest tie binding an infant to its mother. Actually the infants followed a third course. All of them, including those fed from the wire mother, showed an unmistakable preference for the cloth-covered mother, and passed hour after hour huddled against her, clinging to the cloth. The cloth, in brief, gave pleasure, security and emotional support; the nipple satisfied only when the infant had to suckle.

It is significant that the infants displayed so strong an urge, not just to grasp but also to huddle against the cloth. For this urge also reflects the situation an infant monkey confronts in the wild. It must obtain food, it must have protection. The source of both benefits is its mother, and therefore the closer it stays to her, the safer and better fed it will be. Not only that, it *likes* to huddle against her because this makes it feel secure. Does this good feeling come because it has learned that the mother's presence means protection? The truth is not so simple. As Harlow showed in another classic series of experiments, the sense of reassurance an infant monkey obtains from its mother is not derived from her living, breathing, loving presence alone; it is derived in large part from the texture of her body.

Once again, the evidence can be stated very simply. Taking his infant rhesus macaques out of their cages, Harlow introduced them into a large room which contained several strange objects, such as door-knobs and pieces of paper, and one calculated to scare the infants silly: a toy teddy bear which, when wound up, advanced across the floor, beating a drum. The rhesus macaques fell into paroxysms of terror. Some crouched doubled with their hands over their heads while others threw themselves face down on the floor, screaming piteously. Then Harlow added to the scene the cloth-covered mother the infants had grown used to. Instantly, the entire situation was transformed. The infants rushed to the mother and buried their heads against the cloth. Then, reassured and curiosity having replaced fear, they went off cheerfully to play with the very objects that had previously terrified them. They also brought the objects back to the dummy mother, as a human infant brings its mother a new toy. What is more, in tests in which the terry cloth mother was put in full view but inside a transparent box, the infants did not even have to be able to touch her to obtain reassurance: so long as they could see her, they felt confident.

It would be rash to offer any opinion on whether similar experiments carried out with human infants would produce similar results. Human infants are not monkey infants, and that point should be stressed very firmly before we turn to a description of the relationship between monkey mothers and their infants in the wild. Otherwise the reader might find himself forgetting it. Nobody, reading the accounts brought back by field students of how monkeys and their infants behave in the wild, can fail to be struck by the quite extraordinary resemblance to human behaviour. The retreat of the new mother from her normal concerns, the passionate interest of the other females in the new baby, its first recognition of its mother, the play groups, the baby-sitters, the weaning trauma—one after another, all-too-familiar scenes keep recurring.

TAKE, for example, the common Indian langur. We know a great deal about it from field studies carried out by Phyllis Jay, an anthropologist now at the University of California. In October 1958 she went out to India, and during the next two years she concentrated on four separate groups of langurs, three of which lived in forest areas. Being unused to humans, they promptly disappeared whenever Mrs. Jay appeared. Once lost, they were hard to find again in the forest, and she spent a great deal of time merely trailing them around, trying to keep them in sight, before they began to get over their fear of her. Because of the problem of maintaining communication with a troop, she would keep an eye on it until its members had gone to sleep for the night, then return before dawn in order to be on hand when it woke up and began moving again. Eventually the langurs got so used to her presence that her daily arrival did not disturb them at all. Most of the adults ignored her, but many females would huddle against her, hoping to be stroked, and the infants would snap at her ankles or pull at her skirt, trying to lure her into joining in their play.

A good field student gets to know each of the monkeys he is watching. He becomes so familiar with their individual temperaments and quirks that quite often he can anticipate how each monkey in a group will react to almost any situation. This is the basis for understanding monkey behaviour. For once an observer can anticipate a gesture or a movement, he is well on the way to understanding what it signifies. Through months of continually observing the same langurs, Mrs. Jay came to know how each of the females and juveniles and adults would behave to the infants and how the infants would respond, and the following account is drawn entirely from her acute and intensive study.

ALL male langurs inside a group are organized in a dominance hierarchy. So are the females, though to a much less marked degree. As soon as she gives birth, however, a female moves out of the dominance structure. Concentrating exclusively on her infant, she ceases to participate in the group's dominance relationships. If, for example, a squabble breaks out over precedence, she quietly picks up her infant and moves away. As long as the infant requires all her attention, she makes no attempt to impose her will on any other monkey and the others, in return, usually make no attempt to impose their will on her.

Motherhood, in other words, replaces status. As she holds the baby, cleaning and inspecting its body, the other females gather around. Their curiosity is intense and their desire to hold the infant so impelling that they wait in a queue for their turn to do so. A few hours after it is born, the mother allows other females to take it, but her attention rarely wanders from it for more than a few seconds. She will take it back at the first signs of distress or whenever she just feels like holding it. Her right to do so is unquestioned. She can take it away even from a female who is normally her superior in the hierarchy. If ever the group is alarmed, she dashes to the infant, scoops it up and races into the nearest tree. She is able to do this the more easily because the infant is so eager to have her hold it. Soon after its birth, it learns to recognize her and will stretch out its arms towards its mother whenever it sees her approach.

The other females are not merely curious about the new-born infant; they are also extremely protective. Their claim to hold it depends largely on whether they can keep it contented. If it begins to squeal or shows the least sign of discomfort, and if its mother is not near by, another female will take the infant from whoever is holding it. The female's very strong protective feelings are evoked by, among other things, the infant's movements and cries. But hair colour of the baby also plays its part. For the first three to five months, a langur is distinguished by its dark coat, which contrasts with its pink face, hands, feet and ears. Even if its tiny size did not command the attention of the females, its distinctive colouring would. This becomes clear from the way a mother reacts to her infant's death. Apparently non-human primates do not appreciate the significance of death, or so their behaviour suggests. George Schaller once saw a female gorilla carry a dead infant for four days before she abandoned it, and Phyllis Jay saw a langur mother repeatedly trying to make a dead baby cling to her body by placing it under her body and then standing up. When the infant fell, she continued to stroke it gently. But because the mother's behaviour is also a reaction to the infant's movements, the mother of a dead infant gradually gives up. She cleans and inspects it less often, makes less and less effort to retrieve it from other females, and, at last, abandons it completely.

Once the infant's coat changes colour—from dark to light—the attitude of the other females changes. They still come to its aid if it is mistreated, perhaps by a too-vigorously playful older infant, but they no longer want to hold it. Its mother, of course, remains tender and protective, and the infant is never far from her. When the troop is on the move it rides, clinging to her front, and when it stops to feed or rest, the baby stays very close to her side.

All the while, the infant is learning. There is a popular assumption that all animals know by instinct what to eat, where to wander and which enemies they must avoid. So far as monkeys are concerned, this assumption is completely wrong. The infant must learn all that is essential to its survival, such as what it can eat and what it cannot. Just as a young child copies its mother's actions, so does an infant monkey. When foraging, it stays close beside her, picking the same plants and leaves that she does. Actually, juvenile monkeys spend comparatively little time eating. They are enormously active, and work off steam in running, climbing, chasing and wrestling. It is the daylong practice at these skills during an extended adolescence that helps to shape the young monkey into what he will become. As Sherwood L. Washburn and David A. Hamburg have stated in *Primate Behavior*: "The rich social life and environmental exploration by the young monkey or ape is the result of its doing far more than it needs to do for immediate utilitarian purposes. Prolonged youth would have no advantage unless the inner drive to activity led to knowledge and skills."

Observation of others—including mistakes and misfortunes of others—produces a kind of group knowledge among monkeys which is very useful to them. Valuable information is quickly passed around, as is well illustrated by a group of baboons living in Nairobi Park. They had long become used to motor-cars, but when two members of the group were shot from a car, all of them became extremely suspicious of all cars. Eight months later it was still impossible to get near them by car. In the same way, other groups of baboons have learned to flee into trees when threatened by lions, but to come down out of them and run away when threatened by men—although it may be years since the group was shot at. The younger members have learned what to avoid, and the behavioural adaptation persists.

THE mother monkey must learn, too, how to be an effective mother. Though females are born with strong maternal tendencies, the tendencies are only potentials. To be realized, they have to be developed. Long before they are mothers themselves, they learn, by observing their elders, how infants should be treated. Moreover, as juveniles, the females of some species, such as langurs, gain practical experience by holding and looking after the infants of other females. This does not mean that all monkeys are good mothers. Experience helps, of course. A mother who has had four infants is likely to be a thoroughly competent mother. Relaxed yet firm, she holds her baby almost as if she were oblivious to its frequently violent struggles. But there are some females, nervous, uncertain or irritable by temperament, who never make good mothers. In baboons these tend to be the mothers who are low in the female hierarchy and are constantly under pressure from their social superiors. They are continually jogging the infant around, either because it annoys them or because they simply cannot learn how to handle it properly. The unfortunate infant, it need hardly be said, is liable to grow up insecure and irritable itself. Among monkeys, as among humans, the child is "mother" of the man.

As soon as it can walk with ease, a langur infant starts to venture away from

3 WEEKS

5 MONTHS

10 MONTHS

THE BABOON COLOUR SHIFT

A baboon is born with a pink face, pink ears and a black coat of body hair. This colour combination stirs strong reaction in adult baboons; a baby receives intensive care from its mother, and the males of the troop are fiercely protective towards it. Then at four months its face starts to darken and its coat becomes predominantly brown. At this point the mother's interest is rapidly waning, but the males are still strongly protective. By the time the young baboon is ten months old it has all the coloration of an adult. It leaves its mother frequently and seeks out the company of its peers.

its mother and to play with other infants. In most monkeys, births are not evenly spaced throughout the year but tend to occur at certain seasons so that, in a group of any size, there will be several infants in the same age group. While they play, their mothers sit calmly by and watch, like human mothers in a park, intervening only if the play gets too rough. Then they will bring the offenders to order with a mild threat. And, occasionally, some of them will wander away to take a break, leaving one or two behind who watch the babies.

It is hardly possible to exaggerate the importance of play to an infant monkey. It seems obvious that it is through play that the infants learn to adjust to their fellows and become effective members of the society. Being a social animal, a monkey has to learn the rules. Only by trial and error, constantly repeated, does it learn how far it can go in asserting itself—in threatening or attacking others before drawing punishment down on itself. And the play group is the perfect instrument for such learning because its members are young and their teeth are neither sharp enough nor long enough to inflict serious damage,

Inside this protected environment the infant learns how to mix. By playing with its peers, it also develops a fully integrated personality. The word personality may appear somewhat inappropriate when applied to a monkey, but no other adequately suggests the complexity of a monkey's nature. Like humans, they can be social, anti-social, or, in captivity, positively unable to cope with society. They can be well adjusted, neurotic or psychotic. Lower mammals, such as rats, can be driven insane if subjected to sufficient stress. What distinguishes monkeys—and probably apes—from other non-human animals is that artificially imposed stress is not necessarily needed to turn them into neurotics or psychotics. If they do not receive enough of the right kind of care in early infancy, they will never be able to mix properly with other monkeys.

This, too, has been established by Professor Harlow in another classic series of experiments which demonstrates once again how useful the laboratory can be in confirming or elucidating the observations of field students. It is obvious, from watching monkeys in the wild, that they play a great deal. As practically every major activity a monkey indulges in serves some useful function, it follows that play, too, must be important to it. But how important? The only way to answer that question is to deprive monkeys of the opportunity to play and see what happens; and that is exactly what Harlow did.

First he raised several groups of monkeys from birth without allowing them any chance to play. Some groups were brought up in total isolation. The others were raised, each in its own cage, in sight of other monkeys but without any physical contact with them. The results were utterly disastrous. All the infants in both groups developed severe neuroses, or perhaps psychoses. Some sat blankly in their cages, staring fixedly into space. Others clasped their arms and rocked and swayed hour after hour, or sucked compulsively at their thumbs or fingers, or pinched repeatedly at their skins. And some, when approached by humans, chewed and tore at their bodies in terror until they bled.

YOUNG GORILLAS AT PLAY

Play is important to young gorillas as a way of gradually learning the skills necessary to adult gorilla life. It goes on until about the age of six, and has been intensively studied in the wild by George Schaller, whose drawings of young gorillas at play are shown here. In the first picture a 15-month-old infant places a spray of lobelia leaves on its head. The juveniles in the centre are performing a sort of snake dance. Schaller has also observed games of follow-my-leader and king-of-the-mountain. The three acrobats on the right are engaged in the commonest type of solitary play exercise— which builds up muscles and improves coordination. Besides climbing and swinging from branches, they also delight in jumping, sliding, running and somersaulting.

We shall consider in a later chapter the bearing of this behaviour on the genesis of human neuroses and psychoses. For the moment, we are concerned only with the monkeys. After varying lengths of time, Harlow brought them into contact with other monkey infants. Those raised in isolation were simply terrified, completely unable to make any kind of social contact. The infants raised in sight of other monkeys did a little better: they did succeed in establishing some kind of social relationship, but the relationships were thoroughly unsatisfactory. The infants fought savagely, they showed almost no sign of friendliness and, most curious of all, they were unable to copulate.

Why should these monkeys have been unable to perform an act, normally considered instinctive, which is essential to the survival of the species? Two possibilities at once offer themselves. The first is that an infant monkey needs proper maternal care if he is to grow up normal enough to copulate. The second is that monkeys may learn how to copulate in the wild by observing their elders. Harlow, a great believer in testing theoretical assumptions by practical experiment, proceeded to do just that. He raised many infants, males and females, each one alone in a cage with its mother. After several months, he brought the infants together and found that they had absolutely no inclination for making effective social contact. It seems that the presence of the mother is not enough.

That disposed of the possibility that proper mothering is the essential prerequisite for effective sex. Meanwhile, Harlow had also been raising two groups of four other infant macaques. Each was brought up alone in his own cage, except for the presence of a cloth-covered mother. These infants, however, were allowed to play with each other in a large room for 20 minutes a day. The effects of just this brief play period were surprising. After a brief, initial uncertainty, each group of four infants played together with all the confidence, vigour and liveliness of monkeys born in the wild. Nor was that all. Before a year was out, the males and females began to take on their normal roles. The males started to display dominance, the females submission, and all adopted sexual postures which indicated that sex was going to be absolutely no problem.

THESE experiments suggest two extremely intriguing conclusions. To a monkey in the wild, a mother's care is essential for its survival. But, so far as its social life is concerned, playing with its peers is apparently much more important than being raised by its mother. Being allowed to play with the other kids, one might say, is what produces a well-adjusted monkey. How far this might hold true of human children also, the reader must be left to judge for himself—remembering always that humans have the ability, through language, to communicate to each other things that animals can only learn by actual performance. But if we restrict the discussion to monkeys, one further conclusion can be drawn. The four infants allowed to play together had never seen adults copulate. Then obviously they do not learn to copulate by observing their elders. Actually, it is not just the specific physical act of copulation a monkey has to learn; he is born with a tendency to perform it. What he does have

to learn is how to get along with other monkeys. For that ability is apparently an essential prerequisite for effective copulation and it can be acquired by a monkey only through play, at an early age, with other young monkeys.

To think of monkey play in human terms inevitably creates a false impression. This play is incomparably more vigorous. By the time a langur is a year old, it can run up a tree trunk, race along a branch and leap over to another tree with more ease than a human acrobat will ever command. In its vigour, and in some of its forms, the play of infant monkeys resembles that of 10-year-old children. They wrestle; they chase each other. They play follow-my-leader, climbing up to a height, perhaps, to jump down into a pool, as infant macaques do. Young chimpanzees play tug-of-war, using a twig as the rope, and George Schaller observed infant gorillas playing king-of-the-mountain with enormous zest, the king kicking his adversaries and stamping on their fingers as they struggled to dethrone it, though without inflicting any real damage.

All this tremendously energetic scampering around is more than just the natural exuberance of youth. It prepares monkeys and apes to cope with sudden emergencies that one day might mean the difference between life and death. The English research virologist A. J. Haddow has described what happened once when a monkey-eating eagle, flying below the level of the tree-tops, swooped without warning on to a tree where guenon and colobus monkeys were feeding. In a flash, the monkeys raced down to safety near the bottom of the tree. No one knows how often eagles attack or how successful they are. But the monkeys' reaction showed that such attacks must occur often enough for them to have learned to flee—and flee instantly, for an eagle attacks so suddenly that the monkeys have only a second in which to escape. In their sudden flight, they must take jumps far more daring than those they would normally essay, and any females who have young infants must first reach for them and snatch them up before escaping down the tree. Descending with such speed, the monkeys must be able to move with extremely acute agility and judgment, for the slightest error would mean a fall, and possible death.

The ability to react with extra speed and precision in emergencies is essential to the survival of any monkey species, and it is acquired through the long hours of play in which monkeys indulge when they are young. Playfulness, of course, is common among many kinds of mammals, but probably none of them spend as much time at it as monkeys do. Like athletes preparing for the one big event which will demand their maximum effort, so monkeys prepare to meet those sudden moments of crisis which may end in safety or in death.

STILL, such crises do not occur too often. Until it is about a year old, a langur's life must be an extremely pleasant one. There are some members of the group it must not approach, and if it gets too obstreperous it will be disciplined. On the whole, however, permissiveness is the rule. The infant is protected and carried by its mother, treated with tolerance by the adult females, and regarded at worst with indifference by the rest of the group. The process of being weaned must therefore come as a profound and unpleasant shock. Certainly the youngster's behaviour suggests so. At first it reacts as if it simply cannot believe that its mother—that loving, protective mother—is actually rejecting it. Indeed, after a preliminary repulse or two, she does allow it to suckle. But gradually, her rejections become more decisive. When it runs after her, she runs away. When followed, she keeps her breasts covered. If it persists, she may, if passive discouragement fails, slap it. The infant throws tantrums. It screams, slaps at her, beats its head on the ground. Lying beside her high in the trees, it lets an arm and a leg dangle loose. "Look", one can imagine the message, "if you won't let me nurse, I'll kill myself. Yes, I will, too."

For several months the struggle continues, quietly ignored by the rest of the group. Though the infant's cries of distress sound, to human ears, exactly like those which at an earlier stage would have brought an adult racing to its aid, they now evoke no response. Inevitably the mother wins, but having to resist her infant's indignant and persistent claims seems often to impose a severe strain on her nerves, making her exceedingly irritable and very bad company for the rest of the group. Weaning an infant, it seems, can be a strain on mother and child whether monkey or human.

Because a langur female may resume her oestrus cycle before her infant has been weaned, she may attract males while the baby is still with her. This can precipitate a most trying domestic situation. While she is copulating, her infant is liable to stand close beside her, in obvious distress, sometimes slapping impotently at the intruding male. Presumably it feels rejected; possibly it is reacting to what must look like an assault on its mother.

The weaning period, in any event, is decisive. It signals the end of childhood. For a while, the young langur, now about 15 months old, continues to follow its mother around and may even still ride on her, clinging to her belly. Its size makes it look faintly grotesque, like a very big man trying to fit himself into a very small car, because its arms and legs are so big that it hardly has room to pack them into the space between its mother and the ground. Still, try as it may, these attempts to remain a baby are doomed to fail. Several months after the weaning is over, its mother gives birth again and her young juvenile must make its own way in the group.

From this stage on, young langurs become segregated by sexes in a way that, once again, irresistibly recalls human society. The female juveniles stay near the centre of the group, close to the adults, mixing more and more intimately with the adult females and their infants. Holding the infants and sometimes

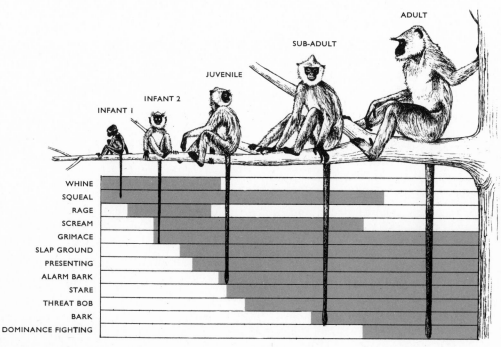

HOW LANGURS COMMUNICATE

As a langur grows up, the kinds of noises and other social behavioural activities that it is capable of keep changing. As a newborn infant, all it can do is whine and squeal. At the Infant 2 stage (from 5 to 15 months), it begins to be able to rage, scream and make grimaces. As a juvenile, it gradually gives up whining and infantile rages and begins to pick up more adult activities such as alarm barks and bobbing its body as a threat. True aggressive barking and dominance fighting are reserved for sub-adults and adults.

tending them while the mothers are away, they are gaining experience towards their own future role as mothers. The male juveniles, meanwhile, spend most of their free time playing. As they grow older, their play becomes ever more vigorous and mobile, and, needing more room, they drift towards the periphery of the group, away from both the adults and the infants.

Through their play, the male juveniles establish the close social bonds that will later help to keep the group unified. As they compete, for food or for the best sleeping positions or the easiest passage-ways through the trees, they gradually establish the order of dominance they will carry with them into adult life. Gradually, too, they begin to have more contact with the older members of the group. One by one, each male sub-adult fights his way up the female hierarchy, dominating one female after another as he grows stronger and more confident, and eventually he will find a position among the adult males. When their period of adolescence finally ends, both females and males are equipped to take their places as fully adult members of the group. Without any formal course of instruction, simply by allowing their own tendencies to develop within the context of the group, they have learned all they need to know.

THE only other genera of monkeys whose youthful developments have been as thoroughly studied are baboons and macaques. The baboon-macaque pattern differs from that of the langur in one very significant way. In a langur group, the adult males behave rather like the traditional Victorian father who kept himself rigidly apart from his young children. Infant langurs grow up in an almost exclusively matriarchal atmosphere. A male langur infant has no contact with the male adults until he is about 10 months old; a female not until she is between three and a half to four. But from birth on, baboon and macaque infants grow up amid a mixed society of males and females who stay together in little clusters whenever the group is resting. Unlike langurs, the adult male baboons are intensely interested in the infants. An infant baboon can play with impunity even with the most dominant male of the group, who is treated practically with awe by most of the older monkeys. And an adult male will frequently approach a mother, smacking his lips to show he means no harm, in order to enjoy the pleasure of playing with an infant.

In fact, young male baboons, from the age of nine months on, tend to have little to do with females, who respond to them less and less as the youngsters get older and increasingly unbaby-like. They also get rough and obstreperous and are smacked harder and more often by the females, and eventually they leave their protection entirely.

Why the difference? It, too, is an adaptation acquired in the interests of survival. Comfortable as some langur species are on the ground, none ever ventures more than a few yards from trees. The females do not require the males' protection and they usually do not get it. If a langur group is alarmed, it is every monkey for itself. Baboons are organized differently, since they frequently move far from the trees, and, if a predator approaches, females and infants alike depend on the adult males for protection. But an animal is hardly likely to risk its life to save an infant for whom it feels no emotion. In the course of their adaptation to life on the ground, baboon males have acquired a tendency to feel affection or at least a strong protective urge towards all infants, and it is this urge that, in an emergency, will give males a motive to defend them. And this is true not only of baboons; the urge to protect their babies must also have evolved in men before they could successfully adapt to life on the ground.

A BRIGHT-EYED, INFANT CEYLONESE GREY LANGUR HAS THE OVERSIZE EARS THAT UNMISTAKABLY SET OFF THE YOUNG FROM THE ADULTS.

Growing Up to Be a Monkey

From their birth to around the time of their weaning, infant monkeys receive the solicitous care of their mothers, who provide them with nourishment, protection and even transportation. Thus made secure, they come playfully to maturity, learning about life through a fascinating process of adjustment and adaptation, in a range of interactions with their mothers, other adults and their age-mates.

FLINGING OUT ITS ARMS, a Ceylonese langur leaps to another feeding tree. Able to get moisture and nourishment from mature leaves, langurs can live in a variety of vegetation zones.

The Importance of Being One of the Group

For animals as slow to mature and with as much to learn as the monkeys and apes, there are advantages in living together in groups, which, of course, is what most primates do. Whether the members number only a few or several hundred, the group becomes the repository of their experiences, which are then passed on to the new generation. The infant born into a group would thus seem to be at an advantage. During its prolonged youth, it not only has the protection of other members but time in which to learn from them, as well as to rehearse, through play, what it has learned. The arboreal grey langurs of India and Ceylon (*opposite and above*) offer prime examples of the benefits accruing from life in a group. Some aspects of their free and easy existence are shown in this picture essay.

PERCHED IN A TAMARIND TREE, Indian langurs display their sleek lines. Although adapted to an arboreal way of life, they often spend as much as 80 per cent of the day on the ground.

TIRED OUT, an infant Ceylonese grey langur leans against its mother. One month old, it still spends most of the day either touching or clinging to her, occasionally climbing on to her shoulders or her head.

IN A RELAXED MOOD, Ceylonese langur mothers groom each other, while their infants—a male on the right, a female on the left—explore their surroundings, licking, smelling and touching strange objects.

In Mother's Shadow

Nothing could be more important to the development of an infant Indian langur than its relationship with its mother. During its early weeks, it depends almost completely upon her, and she, in turn, fastens her attentions upon it—although from time to time she will allow the other females to hold and fondle it. Secure in this maternal haven, the infant gradually comes to widen its horizons. Though its first week is spent sleeping and nursing, by its second it is already stumbling about and being restrained by a yank of the tail or leg. At four weeks, tripping over itself, it ventures forth and discovers the world—or at least that part of it that lies within a safe three or four feet of its mother's side.

CLUTCHING A DEAD INFANT, an Indian langur shows how strong the maternal drive is in a monkey mother—this one carried the corpse around with her for at least two days.

An Ever-widening Circle

As its excursions into the world grow bolder, the maturing infant Indian langur begins to encounter age-mates. At first, with its attention span still short, its co-ordination still imperfect, it retreats from such social contact, scampering "home" for a drink of milk before settling down to play by itself. But by its third month it need no longer rely entirely on its mother. It now learns how to eat solid foods by sampling those the mother consumes (*opposite*), and, in a demonstration of its increasing freedom, spends more and more time away from her side in the company of other young monkeys. This loosening of ties corresponds to a change in the colour of the infant's coat, from brown to light grey. At five months it ranges 20 to 30 feet from its mother for 20 minutes or so at a time, climbing tree trunks and branches, and engaging in play. But despite its new-found independence, the infant is still under its mother's care, still under her watchful eye.

AN ALOOF MALE eating alone on a branch reflects the separation the adult males maintain from the infants. Even in times of greatest danger, they generally do not go to their rescue.

AN ENGROSSED FEMALE ignores the pawing of her infant to concentrate on a mango. Sharing food is not part of maternal care: the infant must learn by copying to take care of itself.

HUDDLED TOGETHER, adult females, an infant and a juvenile form a tight social unit. It is in such groupings that the infant has its first prolonged experience with other young monkeys.

101

Rehearsing for Adulthood

Growing up involves long hours of play, in groups of two, three or more. The young monkeys jump, wrestle, chase each other and pull each other's tails. As they become older, they grow more mischievous, teasing the adult females, jumping on them, bumping up against them, and grabbing their hair or swinging from their dangling tails. By the time Indian langurs reach their 10th month, they are spending upwards of four hours a day hard at play and often travel together, rather than with their mothers, when the troop moves from one area to another. Unlike the females, the young males now begin to have contact with the older males—but almost always in the same highly stereotyped manner. Screeching, they first touch the adults, then tensely they mount them, and finally run around and embrace them.

About this time, when life would seem to be at its very best, something untoward happens—the infants begin to be rejected by their mothers as part of the two-to-five-month weaning process. No longer able to run to their mothers at every scare, no longer protected by them when threatened by adults, the weaned infants—or juveniles, as they are called—must learn to solve their own conflicts themselves. And in doing so they become fully fledged members of the troop—and eventually grown-up monkeys.

ENGAGING IN A LITTLE MONKEY BUSINESS, A YOUNG FEMALE TAKES A SWIPE AT AN ADULT FEMALE'S TAIL —AND THEREBY GIVES AWAY HER AGE, SINC

A STARTLED JUVENILE, its teeth bared, snarls at an intruder, taking it so much by surprise that it bounds upwards. Such threats among the young are often a part of play. Adults threaten by opening their mouths and grunting or belching, by tossing their heads and biting the air, or, when they really mean it, by lunging at each other and slapping the ground.

PLAYFULNESS IS TYPICAL OF SEXUALLY IMMATURE LANGURS. AMONG THE YOUNG, GRABBING TAILS IS A FREQUENT FORM OF PHYSICAL CONTACT.

ADULT MALE BABOON ON THE RIGHT WATCHES ATTENTIVELY AS A FIGHT STARTS AMONG JUVENILES OF A TROOP IN THE AMBOSELI RESERVE

5   Life in the Group

ENYA. IT WILL INTERVENE IN THE FRACAS IF THE YOUNG BABOON BEING CHASED SHOULD, IN TURN, ATTACK THE SMALL JUVENILE IN THE CENTRE.

On the side of a steep mountain on the Japanese island of Kyushu, where bushes and trees sprout thick among the boulders, there lives a group of Japanese macaques—the monkeys of Takasakiyama. They have split up now into smaller units but in 1952 they formed one single, integrated unit, about 200 strong. Their discipline was surprising. In the morning, the group would set out from its sleeping sites on the upper slopes of the mountain to a feeding station established by Japanese zoologists at the base. They walked always in the same order: the young males frolicking on ahead and at the sides, the dominant males walking in the centre, together with the females and infants. They fed always in a similar order of rank: the dominant monkeys first, then the others in descending gradations of status. And at rest, the dominant males, surrounded by females and infants, occupied the most attractive area in the middle of the feeding station, where no subordinate males were allowed to encroach on pain of severe chastisement.

There is no mistaking a dominant male macaque. These are superbly muscled monkeys. Their hair is sleek and carefully groomed, their walk calm, assured and majestic. They move in apparent disregard of the lesser monkeys who scatter at their approach. For to obstruct the path of a dominant male or even to venture, when unwelcome, too near to him is an act of defiance, and macaques learn young that such a challenge will draw a heavy punishment.

To be dominant means to a monkey that it gets the best of everything. It is easy to test the status of two macaques: all one has to do is toss some desirable object between them and see which one takes it. Once, for example, a tangerine was thrown midway between Jupiter and Titan, the two most dominant males of the Takasakiyama group. While Titan remained still, Jupiter, showing absolutely no sign of hurry, rose, walked calmly over and took the tangerine. Another was thrown, this time right between Titan's feet. Once more Jupiter padded over and took it while Titan stood immobile. Later, another tangerine was thrown and it rolled several feet away from Jupiter to the number five male, Monku, who was injudicious enough to stop it. With this implied claim to the tangerine, Monku's act was sheer defiance. Jupiter rushed at Monku and Monku promptly fled.

Jupiter did not press home his attack. For just as he was about to be cornered, Monku stopped, turned his hindquarters and stood passive while Jupiter calmly mounted him, as he would mount a female. Among these monkeys, mounting is the supreme assertion of dominance and presenting the hindquarters is its complementary admission of inferiority. By submitting to Jupiter's mount, Monku was admitting his lower status and seeking to stave off an attack. And Jupiter, having asserted his dominance, could afford to spare Monku from actual physical chastisement.

THIS kind of symbolic assertion of power is common among monkeys. It saves the dominant animals from wasting their energy and the subordinate ones from suffering unnecessary pain. Yet not to assert dominance is to risk losing it: power not exercised is all too likely to degenerate into power lost. Suppose a dominant macaque does not want a tangerine. If he allows an inferior to take it, his charity might be construed as weakness. Symbolic assertion is the ideal solution. When Pan, the number three male of the Takasakiyama group, did not want a tangerine that was tossed between himself and Monku, the number five, he first went over and mounted Monku. His dominance made clear, he then allowed Monku to take the tangerine.

Every morning, when the dominant males reached the feeding station, the animals of lower rank were mounted by animals of higher rank to show who was master. This kind of regular status parade has never been observed among any other group. It was, no doubt, a symptom of the exaggerated competitiveness that afflicts monkeys when they must crowd in to feed in a restricted area. But among all monkeys that have been studied in the wild, a dominance hierarchy does exist, forming a framework on which all social relationships depend.

Take, for example, space. One would imagine that in the forests or on the open savannah a baboon, say, could have all the space it wanted. Actually the amount of space a baboon can command directly reflects its status. A dominant animal controls the space around it; a dominant baboon occupies the best site when a group is resting, and asserts an exclusive right to more space than its inferiors. It can invade an inferior's space as a right, whereas no inferior would dare to venture into its space without first making a gesture of appeasement— such as a smacking of the lips—to show its intentions were friendly. It knocks at the door, as it were, before entering. If the dominant monkey is in an irritable mood, the others give it a wide berth. If it is feeling amiable, they come closer. One can, after all, sometimes chat with the boss.

Or take grooming, perhaps the most commonly observed form of social contact between simian primates. One monkey grooms another by picking through its hair to clean out the dirt and the parasites. Physically, grooming is simply a cleaning mechanism, and it is highly effective, as one can see by comparing lions and baboons which inhabit the same areas of the East African savannah. Although lions are clean animals, the backs of their necks, where they cannot reach to clean, are thick with ticks, whereas the baboons' hair is totally free of them.

To primates such as chimpanzees or gorillas, whose social relationships are comparatively relaxed, grooming is essentially a form of hygiene. They do not spend much time at it, and they normally groom only that part of the hair another animal cannot reach for itself. In sharp contrast, the more aggressive baboons and macaques have adapted grooming to serve as an instrument of social harmony. Much as humans gather in conversation groups, these monkeys gather in grooming groups. The same function is served—the maintenance of friendly social relations. Being groomed is obviously an enjoyable process. The groomed animal sits or lies in an attitude of beatific contentment, like a woman having her hair combed or a man enjoying a scalp massage in a barber's chair. Most of the grooming is done by females. Equals groom each other in approximately equal amounts, while subordinates groom their social superiors much more frequently than they are groomed in turn. As one might expect, dominant males get the most grooming and give the least. There is, however, a semblance of reciprocity, which might be called "pump-priming", in a female's grooming of a male. After she has worked over him for perhaps 10 minutes, she will turn and sit, inviting him to groom her. The male obliges by grooming her for about 30 seconds, then turns indolently and is groomed by the female for another 10 minutes. The significant function of grooming in monkey society is that it cuts across hierarchical lines, establishing friendly relationships without reference to dominance status.

The existence of a hierarchy helps to assure order and discipline, and these things are important among monkeys just as they are among humans. They permit, first, the making of quick decisions. Whenever people are brought together, they will only be able to reach decisions quickly if some kind of hierarchy is established. Every jury needs its foreman; every football team a quarter-back. The same is true of monkeys. Some animal has to decide when the group shall move, which direction it shall follow, what action it shall take to avoid predators. Some form of leadership is essential if action is to be taken quickly, and the hierarchy has come into existence to avoid the total inertia or, at best, the protracted wrangling which is the inevitable consequence of total equality.

The second purpose achieved by the hierarchy is the preservation of the peace.

For total anarchy is another consequence of absolute equality among any group of primates living in close contact with one another. And if the primates are aggressive, anarchy will keep them in a continual state of turmoil. The rigidity of the hierarchy varies, therefore, with the aggressiveness of the species. Though arboreal monkeys, such as langurs, are organized into a hierarchy, it is a comparatively benevolent one. A dominant langur will assert itself over its inferiors; it will push them aside to get the best sleeping site or right of way along a trail. But langurs assert and maintain their status more by bluff than by force, and they almost never get involved in actual physical conflict. The behaviour of a group of gorillas illustrates equally well how an effective hierarchy can be maintained among animals which have little tendency towards violence. Every group has a leader, and each subordinate possesses its own individual status. But though the gorillas inside a group occasionally squabble and bicker, as langurs also do, they seldom if ever settle arguments by force.

To turn from gorillas to baboons and macaques is rather like leaving a Sunday school picnic and driving into an army compound. These monkeys have acquired an aggressive temperament as a defence against predators, and aggressiveness cannot be turned on and off like a tap. It is an integral part of the monkeys' personalities, so deeply rooted that it makes them potential aggressors in every situation. A macaque does not struggle to dominate its fellows because it consciously desires to sit at the centre of the group and enjoy its pick of the females. It dominates every monkey it can because it is a fighting animal.

So urgent a drive to dominate means inevitably that any group of baboons or macaques is constantly threatened from within by the danger of disruptive conflict. They live, as they normally do, at peace only because that peace is enforced by the dominant males. In addition to defending the group against external attack, these males serve also as a police force, and whenever a squabble breaks out, one of them is liable to come running over to stop it.

A dominant male does not usually have to use force. No society could survive if its rulers constantly had to deploy their maximum strength to impose order. If any government employed its full armoury to keep the peace, there would be nobody left to govern, and if the dominant macaques, for example, used the full power of their canines, they would kill off the rest of the group. Instead they preserve order through a system of symbolic threats backed up by their canines, which play rather the same role as a policeman's truncheon.

Suppose that a dominant male is annoyed by a squabble. Its first reaction will be to stare at the offenders. The stare is long and steady, with the animal's whole attention concentrated behind it. If the stare is not enough to quell the trouble, it pulls back the skin on the top of its scalp, drawing back its ears and opening its eyes wide. The movement is a preparation for a fight. It protects the ears from possible bites and allows the animal to see with maximum clarity. A dog, of course, lays back its ears in preparation for a fight in the same way. But these monkeys have carried the process a step further. The preparation has become ritualized to serve as a threat, like a man taking off his coat when an argument gets hot. If the facial threat is still not enough to impose order, the male stands erect, with its body tensed and the fur on its mane stiffened. A baboon may grunt, take a few steps forward, slap the ground threateningly and take a few more steps. Finally, if it still feels defied, it will give chase. When it has caught the offending monkey, it may simply pin its inferior to the ground to show superiority, like a wrestler who wins by pinning his opponent's shoul-

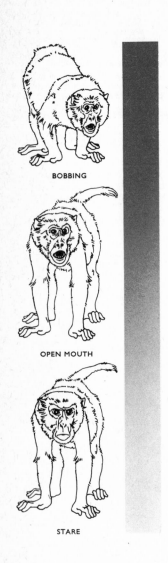

BOBBING

OPEN MOUTH

STARE

THREAT THERMOMETER

Macaques express their aggressive feelings by three basic attitudes. These are of increasing severity, as the coloured graph at the right of the drawings shows. First, and mildest, is the stare—a hard look serving to intimidate. If it does not, the macaque adds extra menace by opening its mouth and showing its teeth. If the target of this enmity is still unimpressed, the last and presumably most terrifying gesture reinforces the facial threats—a bobbing up and down of the head. This is the climax; from then on there can be only fighting or fleeing.

ders. If sufficiently aroused, it will bite, but even this bite is directed to the thick skin at the neck and very rarely draws blood.

All this happens very quickly, but usually it does not all happen, especially if the threatening male is clearly dominant. The higher its status, the fewer threats it has to employ. The threatened monkeys normally either stop squabbling and assume an innocent air, or else they run. On being threatened by a definitely dominant monkey, a subordinate is likely to display submission. Confronted with the fixed stare, it will look away. Faced with a possible charge, it is likely to crouch close to the ground, its head turned away. And if it flees and is chased, it will cringe away from the threatened bite or try to avoid punishment by presenting its hindquarters, as Monku did to Jupiter.

The whole elaborate structure of dominance and submission, of threat and surrender, is surely terribly familiar. It is like a preview, a parody of status relationships between humans. The disciplinary glare of the dominant male closely resembles the stare of a schoolmaster enforcing order in class. The subordinate looking away is the weak man, trying to avoid the challenging glance of a bully in a bar; its flight and surrender crouch are those of a schoolboy begging a stronger boy not to hurt him. The dominant male's authoritative stride is like a general's; its subordinates, carefully stepping back out of its path, could be junior officers. And its decisions, because of the fear it inspires, go largely unquestioned, as do those of a company director delivered to junior executives who are reluctant to disagree with him.

Since the dominant males get the best of everything, why do the subordinate ones put up with life inside the group? Why don't they leave? Why, in other words, does the group stay together in the first place? Until half a dozen or so years ago, it was generally assumed that the members of a group were bound to each other by the urge to satisfy their sexual needs. In many mammals— deer are among the most familiar examples—males and females are together only during the breeding season, forming separate societies during the rest of the year. Since it was generally believed that monkeys were active sexually the whole year round, it was argued that sex was a logical explanation for their staying together. Actually, as recent field studies have shown, many monkeys breed only in a specific season—for example, the rhesus and Japanese macaques— so this simple explanation has had to be abandoned: the closely knit monkey societies continue even when there is no primary sexual activity.

Thus, once again, the study of captive animals proved a misleading guide. In the controlled environment of a laboratory, a monkey's endocrine system, which governs its sex hormones, is not subject to seasonal variations, and the monkey can copulate all the year round. In the wild, its hormones are influenced much more heavily by such external factors as day length, humidity and diet, and the result is that he copulates during only a few months of the year. This is one means of ensuring that the young will be born at an auspicious time, when they are most likely to survive.

Even if the males could copulate all the year round, the females cannot— or at least, they do not. Consider, as an illustration, the female langur. She is not sexually receptive when she is pregnant—approximately one-quarter of her adult life. Nor is she sexually receptive when she is lactating or nursing her young—another third of her adulthood, or, normally, when weaning them—another fifth. Even in the brief periods between pregnancies, she is sexually receptive for only five to seven days in every month, which means

BEFORE

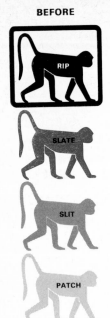

AFTER

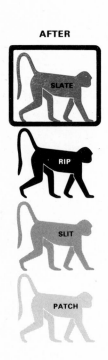

DOMINANCE IN LANGURS

The order of dominance among male langurs is a relaxed one, with the most dominant male (here enclosed in a rectangle) at the top. In this actual field study by Phyllis Jay, Rip, shown in black, was the leader of the male social order, a position he held uncontested for months (before). Then gradually tension developed between Rip and Slate, shown in colour. Slate pressured Rip with whoops and belches until finally, after about three weeks, he had taken Rip's place (after).

that, *in toto*, she is sexually active for only 1 to 3 per cent of her adult life.

Given these circumstances, sex can hardly be the principal element that holds a group together. The real cement is the urge to protect and to be protected, and also to enjoy the sense of ease that comes from living among familiar faces. To monkeys, as to most men and women, old friends are the best friends. Most important of all, the group provides a secure environment in which young monkeys can grow up in safety until they have learned enough and are strong enough to assume their own places in the group. The cohesiveness of a group, in fact, directly reflects the potential danger that threatens its members. Gorillas live in comparatively little day-to-day danger, so individual male gorillas feel free to go off on their own, and many do, even for weeks at a time. The situation among chimpanzees, which are also in little danger, is less clear because they live in such dense forest that no one has yet succeeded in keeping track of all the members of a population in an area. But apparently they split into small units whose membership is constantly changing. Nor do chimpanzees seem much concerned with the general safety, because, when alarmed, an individual chimpanzee will often make off without even giving a warning call.

Such behaviour would be inconceivable among macaques or baboons. However put-upon it may be, a baboon or a macaque is absolutely loyal to its group and, with few exceptions, passes its whole life in the one into which it was born. And actually it doesn't suffer very much. Firm though group discipline may be, the existence of a subordinate baboon or macaque is far from intolerable. Living together from birth, the members of a group learn how to get along. Those who cannot stand each other keep at a distance, and, when tensions do arise, the monkeys involved usually stay apart until tempers have cooled. Only the attempts of one male to displace another in the hierarchy precipitate really vicious fighting, and such occasions are rare. They crop up perhaps once every few months inside even a large group. Because every monkey does know its place, daily life is fairly peaceful.

For it is uncertainty that creates conflict. The hamadryad baboons in the London zoo fought with such savagery largely because they were strangers trapped and brought together from different groups, and they were too closely confined to avoid each other until differences could be settled more amicably. In the wild it is the females who do most of the bickering and squabbling. For while the male hierarchies are rigid, the position of the females is constantly shifting: their status is less clearly defined. This is largely due to the fact that the behaviour of a female is closely tied to the different phases of her reproductive cycle. As long as a female has a young infant she is so closely protected by the adult males that she is not subject to attacks from other females; during motherhood she is, in effect, outside the female dominance hierarchy. A female in oestrum is quite another matter. The word oestrum is derived from the Greek *oistros*, a gadfly, and implies the frenzied behaviour of an animal stung by such an insect. The oestrus female is far more active than normal, both attacking other females and being attacked by them more frequently. Furthermore, when she is most attractive to the adult males, at the height of her oestrus period, she is often under the protection of an accompanying male and can use the status she derives from him to dominate a female normally superior to her. The result of this unstable female hierarchy, and its frequent disruptions, is the constant minor bickering characteristic of female baboons and macaques. Despite all this, adult females of a group do have a basic rank and can be subdivided into a cluster of dominant and a cluster of subordinate females. A few females even sit with the dominant males. But none of these ever quite commands the full authority of a male, any more than the wife of an M.P. commands the authority of her husband, though she may outrank lesser wives at dinner parties.

Whatever the cause, quarrels are always disruptive, and continuous disruption would endanger the group's safety. The peace therefore must be maintained, and among baboons and macaques, peace is simply another word for preservation of the *status quo*. Like the rulers in a human society, it is the dominant males who have the greatest vested interest in preserving it. They do not, of course, labour to do so out of conscious decision. They are motivated by inherited tendencies which are automatically developed as they grow up. None the less, the effect is the same as if the dominant males were members of a human aristocracy deliberately working to preserve their inherited privileges.

Aristocracy, of course, not dictatorship. One of the most intriguing aspects of baboon and macaque social life is that the dominant males form a ruling clique and act in concert to maximize their strength. Individually, a member of the clique might be defeated by some male outside it, and the *status quo* seriously disturbed. In self-preservation, therefore, or out of personal loyalty, the members of the Establishment back each other up. When a subordinate male of the Takasakiyama group, thinking that no dominant males were present, was injudicious enough to venture into the feeding area and bite a female, he was instantly attacked by the number three male, Pan, who happened to be sitting behind a rock. Pan, enforcing the power of the *élite*, was immediately backed up by two other dominant males, and together the three severely injured the rash intruder. Inside the *élite* itself, a similar rule holds; the dominant males support the most dominant member. When the number five male, Monku, stopped the tangerine that Jupiter wanted, Jupiter gave chase and was assisted by Pan. Precisely the same kind of discipline by collaboration is practised among baboons, and one often sees two dominant males threatening an inferior: staring together, slapping the ground together and charging together.

Among birds and other mammals—even other monkeys and apes—that are organized into hierarchies, the status of each individual animal seems to depend on the efforts of that individual alone. The system of rule by clique or Establishment is peculiar to baboons and macaques, and one can easily see why it came into existence. Because the monkeys are potentially so aggressive, the peace in a large group can only be preserved by a force stronger than any one animal could command. Moreover, the existence of a dominant clique also provides a solution to the problem of succession which bedevils monkeys and apes as it does human societies. Rule by a single individual is always hazardous. When Cromwell died, the government he had established soon disintegrated. The murder of Caesar plunged Rome into anarchy. The same kind of anarchy is liable to afflict non-human primates which rely on individual leadership, as gorillas do. But what happens when a gorilla leader dies? Frequently the group splits up, its individual members going off to join other groups. And if the leader should suddenly be killed by hunters, the group may not be able to function in this crisis. "I have seen native hunters," wrote the hunter Fred Merfield, "having dispatched the Old Man, surround females and beat them over the head with sticks. They don't even try to get away, and it is most pitiful to see them putting their arms over their heads to ward off the blows, making no attempt at retaliation."

BEFORE

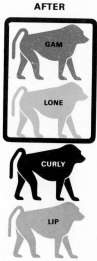

AFTER

DOMINANCE IN BABOONS

In contrast to the langurs, male baboons are aggressive, their hierarchy dominated by groups or pairs best able to combine to rule. Curly and Humbert were such a ruling pair (before), aiding one another when males like Gam threatened their leadership. Then one day Humbert disappeared and Curly was left without his ally. While others floundered among themselves for dominance, Gam and Lone, a male from outside the troop, combined and emerged as the new leaders (after).

Because they have for so long been in much graver danger from predators, any comparable breakdown in leadership among baboons and macaques could, if repeated often enough, have seriously imperilled their ability to survive. The group of dominant males constitutes insurance against such breakdowns. If one dominant male falls sick or is injured or killed, the others simply carry on, incorporating other males into the ruling *élite* as they wish—or of necessity if the challenge of a subordinate on his way up becomes too strong to be resisted. But how does a monkey get into this clique? The question is surely a familiar one to any student of human history and the answer appears to be that entry is won by precisely the same qualities which have traditionally qualified humans for membership in ruling groups.

Strength, first of all, simple brute strength. From the moment it joins its peers in a play group, the young baboon or macaque is continually fighting and jockeying for position. During its subadulthood, it forces its way steadily up the hierarchy, knocking out its rivals like a heavyweight on his way to the top. The battles can be vicious and they are decided by sheer fighting capacity. But muscles and canines are not the only elements involved in the power struggle. The status of a baboon or a macaque is affected also by the strength of its drive and the degree of its self-assurance.

HEREDITARY right, or at least hereditary backing, appears to be a very important element in effecting an entry into the ruling group. Every male baboon and every male macaque has a mother, and each of these mothers has her place in the female social hierarchy. The females occupying the lower rungs of the hierarchy are the ones most likely to be tense, nervous, continually threatened and sometimes attacked by their superiors. It is in this atmosphere that their offspring are raised. Almost certainly, they will take on the attitude of subjection they perceive in their mothers. They grow up afflicted with a sense of inferiority. They lack the style, the manner, the habit and the attitude of the domineering animal; and, as if these drawbacks were not enough, they also lack the entrée to the dominant group.

Somewhat different is the situation of a male offspring of a dominant female, if surrounded by confident, dominant males and females. In this exclusive atmosphere, the infant is likely to acquire the same sense of self-assurance and superiority that its elders display. The family support such a young monkey enjoys continues long past childhood. Field studies have not yet been able to establish which members of a group are related to which others. But most of the rhesus macaques on the island of Cayo Santiago were tattooed with numbers shortly after birth so that records could be kept of their relationships for several generations. According to a recent study by Don Sade, an anthropology student from the University of California, the social groupings of the Cayo Santiago macaques are governed very largely by kinship. Mothers spend most of their time with their offspring and the offspring also tend to stick together long after they have reached adulthood. The result is that any subgroup of the Cayo Santiago monkeys is likely to consist of close relatives—of brothers and sisters and nephews and nieces—so that, for example, the female seen grooming the dominant male of a group often turns out to be his mother or his sister.

As masters of the group, the dominant males usually copulate only with the most alluring females: those who are at the height of oestrum. When a female baboon starts coming into oestrum, she does not at first attract the dominant males, but only the subadults. As her oestrum proceeds, however, the female becomes more attractive to the adult males. With baboons, for instance, the males can observe her condition the more readily because her sexual skin, distended by water retained underneath it, swells up until, at the height of oestrum, she looks as if she is sitting on a cushion several inches deep. At this point, the dominant males are ready to accept her. The arrangement is superbly adapted to group survival because she is now ovulating and the infant she bears, sired by a dominant male, will have the best possible genetic start.

Generalizations about monkeys are as dangerous as generalizations about men and women. To much that has been said about group organization among baboons and macaques, the hamadryad baboons form an exception. No species better illustrates the rule that social behaviour, like anatomy, comes into existence as an adaptation to environment. For the unique social pattern that obtains among hamadryad baboons may very well have been acquired to meet the unique conditions under which they live. All other monkeys—and apes—live in areas where there are normally adequate supplies of food and, always, plenty of trees, so that the members of any one group can easily find safe sleeping sites at a distance from other groups. The hamadryads do not. They are scattered all over north-east Africa and Arabia—for example, places like the near-desert country in the highlands of eastern Ethiopia—living in areas where both food and sleeping sites are in short supply. This situation produces conflicting pressures. The shortage of sleeping sites forces large numbers of the hamadryads to come together at night. Only in that way can they take full advantage of the few sites—such as rocks jutting out from a sheer cliff face—where predators cannot reach them. On the other hand, the scarcity of food may very likely influence the hamadryad baboons to split up into small foraging groups during the day.

CAUGHT between these two forces, the hamadryad baboons appear to have compromised. At night as many as 750 of them will come together to sleep on the rocks. Then, when day breaks, they leave the cliffs in groups of 30 to 50, much like other baboons. But the basic hamadryad social unit is smaller still. It consists of only one male, a few females and their young. The members of these one-male units stick very close together at all times. During the day they may forage in fairly close association with other similar units or they may wander a bit on their own. But they stay always together—even at night, when surrounded by other groups, just as a family on an outing to the Isle of Wight remains a unit though surrounded by thousands of other people.

Still, any family is liable to get split up when caught in a crowd. Facing this danger, the hamadryad baboons have acquired a highly individual form of behaviour to guard against it. The males are exceedingly possessive, and when the hamadryad baboons leave their sleeping sites, each male walks in front of his own little group, constantly looking around to check that his females are following and have not linked up with another male. The younger, less confident males glance back the most often and, if a female drops back too far, they run back and discipline her with a bite on the neck. The spectacle of the hamadryad baboons leaving their sleeping sites is often enlivened by the sight of an anxious male running back and hunting for a female; then, after he has found her and inflicted his bite, by the sight of the screaming female, following close behind him. For she does not really want to escape; the need for cohesiveness has developed in her too strong an urge to follow a male.

Unlike the hamadryad baboons, the dominant males of baboon groups which inhabit the savannah neither need to nor make any effort to keep their females near them; nor do dominant gorillas or, so far as is known, dominant macaques. Such effort is unnecessary because the females want to stay as close to them as they can get. Whenever the adult males prepare to set off, the females immediately follow, and no female baboon has ever been known to leave her group.

Some male baboons and macaques, however, do leave their group if their position in it is made intolerable by the leaders. Possibly their physical strength makes them a danger to the *élite*; possibly personal dislike is involved. A male that finds itself in this unhappy position will be subjected to constant pressure, set upon, harassed and threatened. The situation will be familiar to anyone who ever felt himself to be an outsider at school. In the end, the unfortunate male may be driven out by force, which is what happened to the number six male of a large baboon group in Southern Zambia, who was literally expelled by the top five. The same day, it joined another group, fought and defeated its lone male, and took over its position—very much like a man who is sacked by one company and promptly gets a much better job in another.

More often, a baboon or macaque that leaves its group does so because the pressures gradually become so unpleasant that it finds leaving more comfortable than staying. One such case occurred among a small baboon troop in Kenya, in which the number two male was continually harassed by the number one. Gradually it moved to the periphery of the group and then into the periphery of another. There it stayed for about a couple of weeks, gradually working in closer until, after a few indecisive fights with the males, it joined the group at about place three or four. Because baboon and macaque groups are so cohesive, a male that leaves one group may have to follow another for weeks or even months before it is finally able to enter, and some males probably never do manage to break in.

Yet, for all their intense cohesiveness, baboon and macaque groups do sometimes split up. As the generations pass and the numbers grow, the group may swell to such a size that some kind of a break-up becomes inevitable. It was instability caused by excessive size that finally split the Takasakiyama group. Quite peacefully, when the group had swollen to more than 500, some of the females took their infants and left the central feeding area to join the young males at the periphery. Gradually, the two sections drifted farther apart. They left to eat at different times, and spent less and less time together until, finally, the seceders chose a separate area to sleep in, and the break became complete.

That break was quite peaceful. All the dominant males, from Jupiter down, remained together, and the seceding unit was led by six young males, one of whom became the leader. But the break-up of a group can also be precipitated by internal dissension involving the dominant males. Another group—also of Japanese macaques—has been seen to break up, and in this case the split was triggered when the number three male was displaced by a rising young aggressor. Following this shift in power, severe fighting broke out in the group, and a quarter of the animals—about 50 of them—stopped coming to the feeding place. Led by the deposed and rebellious number three and by another younger male, they formed a separate group of their own. Significantly, the mutinous monkeys obeyed the rules of dominance much more rigidly than the original group had done, as often happens in human society when a revolution occurs and the rebels then emphasize discipline as a counter to the anarchy which is so likely to attend rebellion.

A RELAXED FEMALE ENCOURAGES A DOMINANT MALE TO GROOM HER, WHILE A LESS DOMINANT MALE WATCHES FROM A PROPER DISTANCE.

The Aggressive Baboons

Unlike the arboreal langurs, the ground-dwelling baboons of Africa must constantly guard against predators. Living in large troops, they are organized for defence along lines of dominance and subordination. Despite the intense competition of young males for a place in the hierarchy, each troop, cemented in part by a common interest in protecting its young, remains amazingly stable.

THE DEEP BUT FAST-HEALING WOUND ON THIS YOUNG MALE'S SNOUT BESPEAKS A FIGHT WITH AN OBVIOUSLY MORE DOMINANT MALE.

THE RELAXED YAWN of an old male exposes broken, rotting teeth—a sure indication of its advanced age. However, it is still included in the central hierarchy, despite its worn canines.

If Looks Could Kill

The ability of one male baboon to dominate others is based upon its age, its strength and aggressiveness and the size and condition of its canine teeth. All these enable it to assert itself whenever necessary, which it does by using increasingly severe threats to maintain its authority. The most spectacular threat is shown opposite: here a young male, shoulders hunched and mouth agape, is giving a canine threat, the effect of which it heightens by flashing its white eyelids. Accompanied often by grunting, such a threat is generally sufficient to bring a subordinate quickly to bay—but occasionally, as the wound on the face of the baboon above attests, it is not enough, and actual violence erupts.

THE FIERCE GAPE OF A MALE IN FULL PRIME DISPLAYS CANINES SEVERAL TIMES THE SIZE OF A FEMALE'S.

AGE FACES YOUTH in a brief dominance flare-up. Although it has turned to face its younger, stronger adversary, the old ba-boon (*right*) is extremely frightened—as its screams and erect tail clearly indicate—but for the moment it stands its ground.

HARASSED BY A YOUNG MALE, A FEMALE (CENTRE) ATTEMPTS TO ENLIST THE SUPPORT OF A DOMINANT MALE AGAINST HER TORMENTOR.

Struggling for Room at the Top

The process by which a male baboon achieves a position of dominance in the troop is long and arduous. First the infant male must establish itself in relation to its peers. Then, as a juvenile, it begins to harass the adult females (*below*), who are always subordinate to the adult males. Only after passing through this phase does it finally reach a point where it is old enough, strong enough and skilled enough to make its way into the circle of adult males (*left*). But as many as half a dozen years may pass before it enters the upper level of the male hierarchy. The climb to the top involves numerous attempts to displace other more dominant males, largely through a kind of persistent baiting that sometimes leads to fights, and sometimes even to the backing down of an older and previously higher-ranking animal. Occasionally a threatened male will turn on a subordinate and vent its frustration on this scapegoat; the subordinate may then turn on a male of still lower rank, and so on down the line, in a clear-cut demonstration of who's who in male baboon society.

PUT IN HIS PLACE, the old male continues to scream in an attempt to get aid; the opponent strolls calmly away.

BACKED UP BY MALE STRENGTH, THE SCREECHING FEMALE TURNS WITH IMPUNITY ON THE JUVENILE AND TOGETHER THEY CHASE HIM OFF.

THE EARLIEST RIDING POSITION taken by an infant baboon is demonstrated here by a three-to-four-month-old that hangs upside down from its mother's belly, clinging to her hair.

A FEW WEEKS LATER, the infant abandons its berth under its mother and attempts to ride on her back. But lacking dexterity, it must lie across her and hold on with its hands and feet.

A Mother's Place

A dominance hierarchy also exists among the adult female baboons, although it is a much less rigid one. Unlike a male, a female can rise to the top quite easily—all she need do is give birth. From that moment on, she—or rather, her infant—becomes a focus of interest, the other females and even the males coming forward to look at the new-born. Mother and infant move immediately to the heart of the troop, there to gain the protection of the dominant males in the central hierarchy. With her new importance, the mother is all but immune from the threats of other troop members, and in this sheltered atmosphere, gives herself over to her infant, who will pass through many of the same stages of development as the infant langur discussed in the preceding chapter.

AT ABOUT FIVE MONTHS, the new position mastered, the infant sits astride its mother, nibbling a stem and bracing itself against her tail. When she runs, however, it lies down flat.

SUCKLING, AN INFANT BABOON PRESSES UP TO ITS MOTHER, WHO WILL NURSE IT FOR ALMOST A YEAR.

121

AN AFFECTIONATE THREESOME—a nursing infant, a grooming female and an adult male—demonstrates the basic tranquillity of relations within a baboon troop. Because of the attraction they hold for adults, infants help to bind the members together, gentling even the most aggressive males. Grooming, a social act that knows no social barriers, has a like effect.

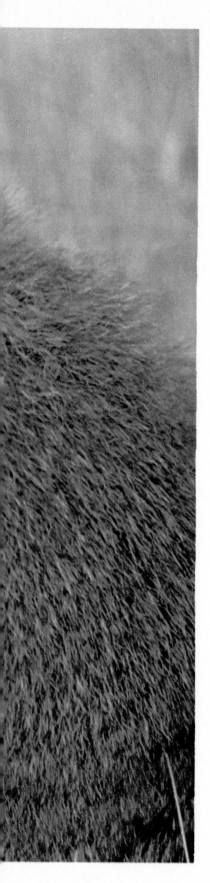

IRRESISTIBLY DRAWN by the sight of an infant, a female approaches the more dominant mother in a properly submissive manner, with rump lowered to denote her friendly intentions.

TUGGING AT A LEG, a young male competes with an older male for an infant—in contrast to the indifference of langur males. Such vying may get rough but never really harmful.

RADIATING POWER, a dominant male strides towards a group of subordinates and elicits an immediate response from three infants that cringe in recognition of his status. Wherever he goes in the troop, such a male commands the respect of all members up to 10 feet ahead.

THE WAYS OF DISCIPLINE employed by baboons in rearing the young are shown here in an encounter between an adult male and an obstreperous juvenile. Punishment is swift and sure (*above*) as the dominant male grabs hold of the erring youngster and gives it a bite on the neck. Such treatment of the young is not as brutal as it looks—the male's teeth fail

SITTING DOWN, thus assuring them of his friendliness, the dominant male is now an object of great attraction to the infants. The chances are he will even engage with them in play, wrestling or letting them climb over him—or at least tolerating attempts to engage him in play.

even to break the skin. Its effect, however, is convincing: the juvenile cowers on the ground squealing (*centre*), while the male looks on and finally (*right*) walks away as the crying juvenile begins to rise. Although extremely tolerant of infants, the adult males begin to take an active role in disciplining the young when these get to be approximately two years of age.

ON ITS OWN, no longer the centre of attention that it once was, a juvenile baboon, aged two, sits in a burnt-over area examining a bit of stubble. Now able to fend for itself, it must also be able to make its own way in the society of the troop—a crucial process which will determine for ever its adult role.

SAFE FROM PREDATORS, a male
baboon adopts the posture it may
keep all night long. Its ischial callosities, or callous pads, bear its
weight and permit it to sleep sitting up even on slender branches.

6

The Group
and the
World Outside

"MAN is born free," runs the famous opening chapter of Rousseau's *Social
Contract*, "and everywhere he is in chains." They are, if nothing else, the
chains of habit. Most of us eat at the same times every day. We sleep the same
regular hours, take the same route to and from work, and live in one town for
much, if not most of our lives. How different, one might imagine, is the un-
trammelled existence of the monkeys and the apes. They are free. No time
clock or commuter train schedule binds them. They can eat or sleep whenever
and wherever they please, stay in one place as long as they wish, wander
throughout the forest as their whim dictates.

Such a picture could hardly be further from the truth. Compared to the
average suburbanite, the life of a monkey or an ape is monotonous, repetitious
and humdrum. By every imaginable standard of comparison, the non-human primates are intensely conservative. They pass their entire lives amid the same small
group of companions. They move to and fro, round and round, constantly re-
treading the same well-worn trails, never venturing beyond one tiny area of
the forest or the savannah. And they follow daily schedules almost as regular
as those followed by many men.

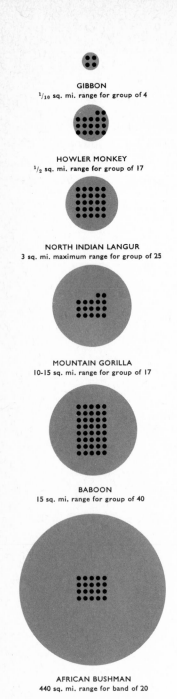

GIBBON
1/10 sq. mi. range for group of 4

HOWLER MONKEY
1/2 sq. mi. range for group of 17

NORTH INDIAN LANGUR
3 sq. mi. maximum range for group of 25

MOUNTAIN GORILLA
10-15 sq. mi. range for group of 17

BABOON
15 sq. mi. range for group of 40

AFRICAN BUSHMAN
440 sq. mi. range for band of 20

HOME RANGES

Tree-living primates tend to have smaller groups and roam less widely than those on the ground. The circles above stand for ranges; the dots indicate individuals in each group. Gibbons and howler monkeys find enough food within small tree-top ranges. Langurs, often feeding on the ground, and the more terrestrial gorillas, exploit wider areas. Baboons on the savannah roam farther—but still not as far as African bushmen, representing Homo sapiens, who can travel and hunt over more than 400 square miles.

Except for one South American species, the douroucouli, or owl monkey, all monkeys and apes are diurnal. Their day begins at dawn. Like many humans, they tend to be sluggish when they first awaken, but very soon the juveniles, then the females and last of all the adult males liven up and start to feed. This, the first meal of the day, continues for some time, interrupted only as the group moves, in search of food, along some familiar trail. Towards midday, they break off for a rest, very similar to the siesta enjoyed by humans who live in warm climates. The adults nap or groom each other or just laze in the shade while the energetic youngsters sport and play around them.

Eating brief snacks throughout the day, the group starts in on its second period of intensive feeding in the late afternoon, continuing to eat steadily for perhaps two hours. Then, as evening approaches, the group slowly begins to make its way back, along the ground or through the trees, to one of the regular sleeping sites, where it will pass the night. One by one, the members of the group climb out to their sleeping places. Gradually their activity dwindles away and, by the time darkness descends, all the animals are asleep.

THE rigid attachment of monkeys and apes to one tiny domain is yet another symptom of their conservatism. The domain, of course, is a three-dimensional one. Different foods and different living conditions exist at all levels in the trees, with each species tending to stay fairly close to the one that suits it best. Gibbons and orangs, howlers and colobus monkeys spend almost their whole lives near the top canopy of the forest. More extreme yet in its vertical confinement is the timid olive colobus. Normally it stays within 20 feet of the ground, but almost never actually descends to it, and climbs higher than 20 feet only to sleep or to avoid predators. Primates with a more catholic diet range farther up and down in the trees, and they also come more frequently to the ground. Horizontally as well as vertically, the more arboreal the primate, the smaller is its range. The gibbon, that supreme arborealist, passes its whole life within the same one-tenth of a square mile. A group of howlers travels over a range of half a square mile. The common Indian langur, which spends much of its time on the ground, roams farther—from one to three square miles. And the greatest wanderers of all are the terrestrial monkeys and apes—the gorillas, the baboons and the macaques. Baboons usually walk three to five miles during an average day. During the course of a year they will travel over an area of from ten to fifteen square miles, constantly crossing and recrossing their tracks as they make their daily journeys between feeding areas, water-holes and sleeping sites.

What governs the limits of a group's range? The answer is that rallying cry of conservatism—the tradition of long habit. As they grow up, young monkeys and apes observe unconsciously that their group never wanders beyond certain boundaries, set by a stream perhaps, by a ridge of hills or by no particular landmark at all. Beyond these boundaries lies the unknown, threatening in its mystery. Reluctant to venture there and conditioned by their early confinement, monkeys and apes continue, when they reach adulthood, to stay within the range they have learned to know.

Generation after generation, the same tradition is passed down, and this tradition is reinforced by the sense of security which comes from living amid familiar surroundings. Like men and women who feel most relaxed in their home towns, a group feels safest and most at ease in the heart of its home range. There it is intimately acquainted with the best feeding places, the safest sleeping sites, the most dependable sources of water. As a group moves towards the limits of its range, its members become progressively more tense, and beyond those limits they never venture. No one has yet been able to drive a group out of its range. Even prosimians will resist any effort to force them over the boundaries because their fear of the unknown land ahead outweighs their fear of the drivers behind. The same is true of baboons, as the English psychologist K.R.L. Hall discovered when he and a co-worker tried to drive a group of baboons out of its range, only to find that when the monkeys reached the boundary they turned and ran back, right past the two people who were driving them.

That group tradition should dictate the limits of the range is no accident. It is an adaptation for survival. Being in competition for the same food, different groups of the same species might well get involved in suicidal fights if they just wandered freely in and out of each other's feeding places. Inherited tradition helps to keep them apart, and it is backed up by a system of signals which is especially useful to arboreal monkeys who, unable to see clearly through dense foliage, might accidentally blunder into each other. As soon as they awake in the morning, the adult males of a howler group set up a steady roar which lasts for up to half an hour. The roar is repeated whenever the group moves from one feeding place to another or when two groups come into contact. Then the males will roar at each other until one group retreats.

Langurs also use signals—whoops in their case—to let other groups know where they are. So do gibbons, while the equally arboreal spider monkeys of South America give warning calls which sound like the bark of a terrier. Obviously this kind of vocal signalling is not needed on the ground where one group can easily see another long before making contact. This is one reason why ground-living monkeys are so quiet compared to the noisy monkeys of the trees. A baboon, for example, uses sounds only for a particular purpose: when it is separated from the rest of the group, to sound the alarm when it sees predators, to threaten, or to keep in touch with the rest of the group when it is feeding in dense foliage.

T HE care a group takes to warn other groups of its presence is yet another symptom of conservatism. Only the familiar is safe: strangers are suspect and their mere presence is cause for alarm. Still, not all monkeys and apes are equally apprehensive of strangers. For suspicion is always defensive, a reaction to danger experienced or anticipated and, as we have seen, the species that are most fearful are also the most aggressive. As one might expect, gorillas and chimpanzees, which have little to fear from predators, are the least perturbed by unfamiliar members of their own species. A resident chimpanzee population will accept stray individuals. Two gorilla groups will often come together quite peacefully and, provided the leaders do not happen to be unusually suspicious individuals, the members of different groups may intermingle freely.

As one moves along the spectrum of fear, suspicion of strangers increases. Howlers and langurs are typical representatives of the next stage. Though not in much danger from predators, they do not feel as secure as gorillas. So if, as sometimes happens, a male howler or langur leaves its group, it may find it extremely difficult to join another. Suspicion of strangers (and its complement, aggression) reaches its peak in baboons and macaques, especially in the rhesus macaque, probably the most aggressive of all non-human pri-

HIGH AND LOW LIFE AMONG THE MONKEYS

Although monkeys are often thought of as ranging widely from the tops to the bottoms of trees, many of them actually spend most of their time at very specific levels in the canopy, each seeking out its own level according to food preference. This drawing illustrates in simplified form the layering of different species of colobus and guenons (shown in various colours). Some species of monkeys have become so accustomed to their particular levels that they will not shift to other storeys even for the same types of food.

COLOBUS

GUENON

mates. The difference in attitude between the more and the less suspicious species was demonstrated very neatly a few years ago when a male and a female macaque joined a group of langurs. The male bore on his face the traces of a healed scar, which suggests that he had been wounded in a fight and had either been driven from his group or had voluntarily decided to leave it. Presumably, being a monkey and therefore highly sociable, he preferred to convalesce among monkeys of a different species to being left entirely alone. Why the female accompanied him to join the langurs is a mystery. Whatever their reasons, the two macaques behaved according to form. Like two refugee soldiers billeting themselves on a village of timid men and women, they established, though hopelessly outnumbered, complete dominance over the langurs.

But this was not all. Though they were living among monkeys of a completely alien species, the refugee macaques retained all their suspicion of strangers. At one point, a lone male langur appeared on the scene and started to wander around the periphery of the group, hoping to break in. Acting like a self-appointed sentry, the male rhesus would draw the attention of his male hosts to the presence of the outsider. Once alerted, the male langurs then joined in repelling the stranger and eventually he wandered away. It is hard not to feel sorry for him, for had it not been for the presence of the rhesus male, he might well have succeeded in joining the group.

THE apprehension and fear that an unfamiliar member of the species can inspire in macaques was illustrated even more dramatically by another incident which took place in the summer of 1964 at the University of California. Above the Berkeley campus, in Strawberry Canyon, there is an animal research centre where a number of monkeys are kept together in groups, each inside its own large cage. Among them are about a dozen crab-eating macaques, which, compared to most other macaques, are quite mild and unaggressive. One afternoon, a group of people, including Sherwood Washburn, the director of the primate section of the centre, was standing in a small, cell-like room, which is separated from the macaques by a wire net. It was a hot, lazy summer day. The macaques were basking somnolently in their cage, and a visitor to the centre was describing an experiment in which an anaesthetized chimpanzee had been shown to a group of nine adult chimpanzees in a cage. They had reacted with great violence to the sight, screaming, spitting and trying to attack the anaesthetized animal. This reaction, the visitor suggested, showed that the chimpanzees obviously shared man's fear of death.

"But how do you know", Washburn asked, "that they wouldn't have reacted just as violently to the sight of a live chimpanzee if it were a stranger?"

The visitor replied that this seemed to him highly unlikely.

"Let's try it", said Washburn. "Let's go fetch Isabelle."

Isabelle is another crab-eating macaque, about two years old, who has never belonged to the group, and is kept in a cage by herself at the top of a hill which leads up from the monkeys' cages. Holding her carefully, because Isabelle is nervous and given to biting, Washburn brought her down into the room. As he came in, two of the other macaques were standing near the netting. At the sight of them, Isabelle let out a small squeak of alarm. The effect was electric. Within a few seconds, all the other crab-eaters were clinging to the netting, a solid mass of alert, frightened monkeys, all gazing spellbound at the hapless Isabelle.

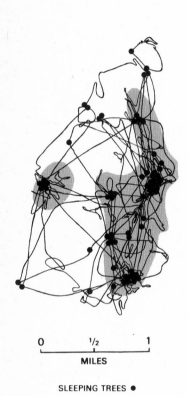

0   ½   1
MILES

SLEEPING TREES ●

THE CORES OF THE RANGE

A group of primates not only limits itself generally to a home range: it spends most of its time in an even more closely defined area within this range. This map by Phyllis Jay shows the many routes taken by a troop of langurs over the whole of their home range in northern India, during an 80-day period. Dots indicate the trees in which the langurs sleep; where the dots are thickest are the so-called core areas (coloured), the most heavily used parts of the range. Besides having plentiful sleeping trees, these core areas provide the langurs with rich supplies of drinking water and vegetation.

There was a very brief silence and then Isabelle gave another call, louder this time, half a squeak, half a cry. The other macaques, normally quite placid, responded with the utmost vehemence. They shook the netting, they threatened furiously, they screamed. They were, of course, threatening Isabelle in a language she could understand and, in her terror, her heart began to beat so rapidly that Washburn decided to take her away.

But the incident was far from over. As soon as Washburn had gone, the macaques left the netting. Half a dozen of them raced up the sides of the cage and clung to a beam which stretches across the roof. The others also took refuge in some distant corner—all except the leader, a four-year-old male, generally known as Fats because he is a compulsive eater and grossly corpulent. Normally, Fats is lethargic; now he was transformed into a dynamo of energy. First he scuttled across the floor to an eyehole from which he could see out and up the hill where Washburn was walking. Then he tore back, raced up one side of the cage and on to the beam, and swung himself out and past the other monkeys until he reached an eyehole in the wall which gave him a better view up the hill.

At this point, the visitor noticed that all the macaques, including Fats, were defecating. It is a sure sign of fear; a gorilla in a zoo was once cured of constipation by being shown the head of a turtle which he mistook for a snake. Yet the sight of Fats, usually so self-assured but now so frightened, was curiously uncanny; the sensation he evoked was precisely what one feels when a grown man bursts into tears.

A few minutes later, Washburn came back. "You see," he said, "they don't like strangers. Even live ones." It was a comment which neatly disposed of the visitor's contention about the chimpanzees.

The macaques involved were, of course, captive animals, reacting in a thoroughly unnatural situation. In their natural state, where there is no overcrowding and food is plentiful, monkeys do not display this kind of intensely aggressive defensiveness. In the wild, members of even the most aggressive species reach a mutual understanding which takes account of their neighbours' need to survive. "You keep out of our hair," is the sense of it, "and we'll keep out of yours." This live-and-let-live arrangement is essential if physical combat is to be avoided. For although neighbouring groups normally avoid each other's central feeding places, they do not necessarily keep apart altogether. Like two families who each possess their own living quarters but who share the same kitchen, two or more groups of baboons will often come together to feed out of the same fruiting tree or to drink from the same water-hole. They share this part of their range in common; obviously the arrangement can work only if the groups are mutually tolerant.

EVEN when drinking from the same water-hole, the two groups do not intermingle. Normally, the smaller one will move away when the larger and more powerful group arrives. But from years of sharing the same drinking water, the members of different groups may come to know each other by sight. More likely, the different groups are the result of peaceful splits in what was once a single group, so that some of the adults grew up together. Continued contact refreshes this familiarity and a limited amount of camaraderie may be maintained between the groups. One young baboon, for example, often used to go off and play with the juveniles of another group encountered at a water-hole, much as a boy might visit the house of a neighbour. And this kind of

TELLING MALE FROM FEMALE

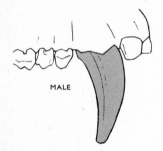

MALE

Because of obvious differences in size, male and female baboons can be told apart at a glance. In addition to being more than twice as heavy as its mate, the male has much larger canine teeth (colour). Among the ground-dwelling baboons, large size and large teeth are essential male attributes since the males must protect the troop from predators.

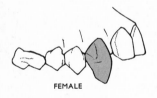

FEMALE

early friendship, no doubt, can make it comparatively easy for the baboon to shift groups later, if for some reason its situation in its own group should become unpleasant.

The pressures of predation have led baboons to develop a mutual assistance programme with animals of different species altogether—principally, in savannah and forest alike, with ungulates, who share with them a common fear of carnivores. Together, baboons and their hoofed neighbours form an alliance whose chief function is a very efficient warning system. As baboons have a keen sense of vision and ungulates possess a keen sense of smell, they are, in combination, almost immune to surprise, and a single warning bark will alert all of them to danger. A group of baboons was once seen in Nairobi Park, feeding on the side of a hill that was separated by an open space from the dense bushes around a water-hole. Two lions came into view, the baboon males gave warning barks, and, within a few seconds, a mass of giraffes, impalas and water-bucks, previously hidden in the bushes, had streamed out into the open, where they stood, nervously testing the air, trying to identify the danger.

THE baboons' own defensive system is an elaborate one, and it is yet another example of how selection for survival can lead monkeys to develop patterns of behaviour which serve a variety of purposes. We have seen how, when they are at rest, baboons take up positions which reflect their personal relationships. The dominant males sit at the centre of the group, near the females and the infants, while the younger and less dominant males stay out on the periphery. When the group is moving, this spacing pattern is maintained; it becomes, as it were, mobile. The dominant males, the females and the infants stay in the middle of the marching column, while the other males either go on ahead in the manner of an advance guard or follow behind.

In this situation, the positioning of the baboons serves as an instrument of group survival. Going on ahead, the young, powerful males are most susceptible to sudden attack; they are also the most expendable members of the group. The defenceless females and infants are closely escorted by the older, dominant males who can best defend them, and if predators do approach, the group will keep moving while all the adult males drop back to form a defensive screen.

A dominant male will also drop back to help a female or an infant in distress, as one was seen to do for a female burdened with a new-born infant which could not cling properly. Compelled to use one arm to hold the infant, she lagged behind the group. Whenever she stopped, her male escort also stopped; when she moved, he moved. He never left her for a moment unprotected. Just how protective a male baboon can be to an infant was illustrated even more dramatically on another occasion when a mother, after carrying a dead infant for several days, finally abandoned it. Immediately a male appeared at her side and barked, and the mother wearily took up again her useless and pitiful burden.

Because effective defence is essential to their survival, baboons learn how to cope with danger with amazing rapidity, and they forget only very slowly what they have learned. Furthermore, it would appear that the frightening experiences of some can be passed along somehow to become part of the experience, the tradition, of the entire group. This ability to pool knowledge is, of course, one of the basic advantages of group living, for it means that individual animals do not have to make their own mistakes in order to learn caution. The young especially can draw the appropriate conclusions from the mistakes or the bad luck of others, and a baboon who is killed does not, one might say, necessarily die in vain. For the mode of its death may have the effect of improving the chances that its companions will survive.

If there is one generalization that holds true of all the monkeys and apes so far studied, it is that they are full of surprises. The observer who goes out to conduct the first study of a species is always liable to return with a sheaf of notes which will astonish his colleagues. Consider, for example, the patas monkey, which for years had kept primatologists baffled. Though adapted to terrestrial life, it is neither tough nor equipped to fight off predators, as baboons and macaques are. Instead, it is a slender, long-legged monkey with a considerable turn of speed, which led primatologists to assume that it managed to avoid predators by outrunning them. Then, in the summer of 1963, K.R.L. Hall carried out a study of patas monkeys living in Murchison Falls National Park in Uganda. One day a group of patas that he was following unaccountably disappeared. Though he searched far and wide over the savannah, he failed to find them—until he returned to the place where he had last seen them. And there they were: instead of fleeing, as he thought they had, they had simply crouched down out of sight in the long grass. Nevertheless, under other circumstances—as when a group of baboons is approaching—patas will run away very fast and far.

The habits of the patas, as Hall has described them, indicate that their adaptation to life on the ground is quite different from that of other ground-living monkeys. Silence, caution and withdrawal are their protection, rather than the long canines and tough fighting qualities of the male baboons and macaques. Instead of remaining always close to each other, as the members of a baboon or macaque group do, the patas monkeys stay far apart at night, so that if one monkey falls victim to a predator, the others will have a good chance to escape. Yet, although their behaviour seems to be unique among ground-living monkeys, the patas' timidity and caution towards man is typical of many other non-human primates. Only those that are habituated to human beings will remain calm when a man or woman approaches. The others will immediately seek refuge in some fashion, perhaps by freezing as the patas do or, more commonly, by beating a hurried retreat.

E VEN the powerful gorilla is afraid of man. Although a male may pause and beat his chest in brief threat when a man approaches, it will very quickly fade back after the rest of its group into the concealment of the forest. The gorillas' nervousness, of course, makes them extremely hard to follow and many people had tried and failed to study them before George Schaller succeeded. Undoubtedly his success was largely due to the remarkable patience and caution he displayed. Until they were thoroughly used to him, for example, he never looked gorillas directly in the eye. Nor did he point a pair of field glasses or a camera at them in case they might have interpreted the staring eye of the lens as a threat.

An individual gorilla could still be exceedingly nervous, as Schaller discovered, even when surrounded by other gorillas who had lost their fear. Once, a strange female joined a group that he had been following for several weeks. The other gorillas were no longer at all scared but whenever the female saw Schaller, she immediately screamed and dashed away. With some amusement, he noticed that the other gorillas appeared baffled by the violence of her reaction, since they had presumably forgotten that he had ever disturbed them. And the female, no doubt, must have been equally mystified by her companions' strange imperviousness to this intruder, a man—the gorillas' one really dangerous enemy.

As the other non-human primates share the gorilla's nervousness, any man or

Male and female gibbons are far more difficult to tell apart than male and female baboons. The male gibbon is only slightly larger than the female, with only slightly larger canines (colour). But gibbons, unlike the ground-dwelling baboons, live in trees and thus have less need to defend themselves; when a predator strikes, it is every gibbon for itself.

woman who wants to get close to them must be careful, as Schaller was, not to perform any action that might appear aggressive. Still, even the best students can slip up occasionally, as Phyllis Jay once did, thereby provoking one of the most curious interactions ever to take place between a monkey and a human being. She had been scrupulously careful not to do anything that might be construed as a threat, until one afternoon, when sitting in the middle of a group of langurs, she turned to get a notebook from her bag and accidentally hit a young female who was sitting close beside her. The langur immediately ran off. Next time the two met, the female turned and presented her hindquarters as if she expected to be mounted. By hitting her, Mrs. Jay had achieved dominance.

One cannot, of course, read the mind of a monkey. Still, the mere fact that the langur reacted very much as she would have done to another monkey certainly suggests the possibility that she sensed the close ties of kinship that connect monkeys to man.

THIS incident, of course, could only have taken place with a person who, with patience and understanding, had succeeded in winning acceptance by the monkeys as something other than a stranger or an enemy. For it is unfortunately indisputable that man is, on balance, an enemy. Every year, hunters capture or kill apes and monkeys by the thousands—for zoos, for meat or for their skins. As man penetrates deeper into the forests and cuts down trees to open up the land for farming, the non-human primates in his way are left homeless. Some species, indeed, like the gentle orang of the East Indies and the mountain gorilla of Central Africa, are in real danger of being wiped out, except for the few pitiful survivors who may live on in the loneliness and confinement of zoo cages.

Still, it would be unfair to state categorically that man's intrusion into their habitats has been, for all monkeys and apes, an unmixed curse. Especially in India, some monkeys may have benefited from man's presence. Because langurs are regarded by Hindus as gods to be worshipped, they have traditionally been allowed to wander at will over the countryside and to feed off any crops that take their fancy. In many parts of India, rhesus monkeys are permitted an equal freedom simply because the people are uncertain which kind of monkey they are supposed to worship. Much more aggressive than the langurs, and able to exist comfortably in a variety of environments, the rhesuses have taken substantial advantage of the confusion. Many prefer to live in or around villages rather than in the forest, probably because it is easier for them to get food and water in the places man has cultivated. Rhesus monkeys can also be found in most large towns with heavy Hindu populations, and they often wreck shops and private homes without suffering any punishment.

Recently, however, the Hindus' traditional tolerance has begun to weaken, and a new *modus vivendi* has been reached with the rhesus monkeys. They are chased away from private property but they are allowed to live undisturbed in public places, along roadsides and canal banks, or in temples and railway stations. If they venture out of these privileged sanctuaries and into privately owned fields or bazaars or residential areas, they are driven back. But as long as they stay in their recognized refuges, they are left in peace. They are, indeed, regarded more as a source of entertainment than as a nuisance, and parents will often take their children along on family outings to feed the monkeys. Custom, after all, is mostly a matter of geography. Allowing monkeys to run free beside the highway might strike the average Westerner as outrageous; but then Hindus no doubt feel precisely the same way about keeping them caged in zoos.

GATHERING AT DAWN BELOW THE TREES IN WHICH THEY SPENT THE NIGHT, A TROOP OF BABOONS PREPARES TO MOVE OUT TO A FEEDING AREA.

The Baboons' World

The life and death of a baboon occurs within a remarkably small area, compared to the ranges of the migratory animals with which it is in almost daily contact. At most, the yearly range of a troop may be no larger than 15 square miles, and even this is subdivided by the members into smaller core areas. But here baboons find all they need—food, water, alert allies and the refuge of trees.

Patterns of Defence

Living out in the open as they do in predator-patrolled country, baboons must be ready at all times and in all situations to defend themselves. The diagram above shows how a troop —here reduced in numbers for simplicity's sake—would be organized for defence when moving to a feeding area or waterhole, at rest or on the offensive. The dominant males on which the burden of defence falls are coloured purple, the subordinate males blue, the females brown, the weaned juveniles rust, the younger juveniles tan and the infants black. When a baboon troop is on the move (*top*), the subordinate males take up positions at the front and rear of the group like expendable outriders. The females and infants stay in the centre with the strongest males close by. At rest (*left*), the troop tends to keep much the same order it had on the march. The dominant males, the females and the infants are still in the centre, but the juveniles are now romping through the troop or playing together at the edge of it. On the offensive (*bottom*), the dominant males emerge from the heart of the troop and take positions out in front, where they lead the other males in action against a predator while the females and young retreat.

DRIVEN BY THIRST, baboons and Grant's gazelles move cautiously past trees and underbrush towards a water-hole. Here, should the shrubbery hide a predator, the keen-nosed, keen-eared gazelles would probably be first to give the warning bark,

A Joint Warning System

One way baboons keep predators from taking them by surprise is to look up, every 5 to 10 seconds, from whatever they are doing and glance quickly around. Their vision is considered to be on a par with man's, although hunters who have tried stalking them would say that it was a great deal better.

The fact is, any hunter trying to stalk a troop would be up against anywhere from 30 to 150 pairs of eyes, each scanning a slightly different part of the area at slightly different times; the chances are he would not go unnoticed for long. Another way baboons guard against surprise attack is to associate themselves

alerted by the enemy's odour or by a noise. But in the open, the sharp-eyed baboons would more likely voice the alarm.

EACH AT EASE in the other's presence, a baboon rests on a rock while two impalas browse; they may stay together all day.

during the day with such ungulates as Grant's gazelles and impalas, whose senses of hearing and smell are far superior to their own. Baboons have learned to recognize the ungulates' warning barks, just as the ungulates have learned to recognize the baboons'. Thus, no matter which of the animals gives the alarm, both kinds will benefit simultaneously. Impalas were once observed feeding with baboons when three cheetahs appeared on the scene. Nervous though they became in their presence, the impalas did not stampede; instead, they stood by while the adult male baboons drove the cats away.

The Makings of a Carnivore

Despite the fact that they are considered to be primarily vegetarian, and are ill-suited anatomically to be efficient carnivores, baboons are known to kill and devour small animals—and occasionally even the young of the ungulates upon which they depend, to some extent, for their safety (*below and opposite*). Such carnivorous activity cannot be prompted by hunger alone, since many of the killings that have been observed took place after the rainy season, when the baboon's favourite plant foods are most abundant. Nor is such behaviour innate; eating meat seems to be something baboons must learn to do. Apparently, many baboons are opportunistic predators, eating a fledgling or baby gazelle found while searching for vegetable fare, but others learn to chase and catch hares or vervet monkeys whenever they have the chance.

HUNCHED OVER A HARE, a male baboon prepares to rip open the belly. In this instance, only 30 seconds elapsed before the baboon had skinned and stuffed the animal into its mouth.

YANKING AT THE ENTRAILS of a baby Thomson's gazelle, which it killed with a quick slam to the ground, a dominant male has first choice before a subordinate male joins the feast.

CRACKING THE SKULL of a dead Thomson's gazelle, a male baboon bites deep to get at the brains, which it will scoop out with its fingers. This done, it will lick and scrape the bones.

A Peaceable Kingdom

In addition to sharing its home range with various kinds of antelopes, a baboon troop gets along equally well with elephants, giraffes and most of the other herbivores of the African savannah. It may even share part of this area with other baboons—the ranges of several troops often overlap. This sharing is usually peaceful. One factor that acts against group rivalry is daily routine; the activities of each group tend to restrict it to a particularly favoured part of the home range. But even in drought, when several troops may come together at a single water-hole, familiar neighbours are closely tolerated and aggression is displayed only towards strangers.

BENDING TO DRINK, baboons and kudu share a water-hole at a game reserve in Rhodesia. Baboons that have already drunk scamper nervously away from the edge of the water.

BABOONS, ZEBRAS AND WART-HOGS FEED TOGETHER NEAR A WATER-HOLE IN THE AMBOSELI PARK IN KENYA. EVEN IN THE DRY SEASON, WHEN FOOD

LUMBERING BY, an elephant dwarfs the baboons near it, but evokes no fear in them. Baboons even feed under trees being denuded by elephants, occasionally stepping out of their way.

TOWERING ABOVE the baboons, the giraffe can see over shrubs, an advantage baboons exploit at water-holes—a giraffe drinking is reassuring proof that no predators lurk in the brush.

S EXTREMELY SCARCE, THE BABOONS SEEM UNDISTURBED BY THE COMPETING WART-HOGS, WHICH ALSO CONSUME GRASS, ROOTS AND RHIZOMES.

The Dominant Males in Action

The animals to which baboons cannot afford to be indifferent are, of course, those that prey on them. But being quick to spot them and quick to organize against them, baboons show surprisingly little fear of these enemies—that is, as long as they remain in the troop and in the vicinity of trees into which they can climb when their threats fail. The sick baboon, or the baboon left behind when the troop moves on, has everything to fear. Relatively small (a dominant male weighs only about 75 pounds, a female half that), it would simply be no match for a large predator and might even be brought down by a wild dog, a hyena or a jackal. The sight of an ailing or maimed baboon trying to keep up with the troop is a pitiful one—and here, too, is a situation in which the dominant male may step in to safeguard a member of the troop. There is a documented case, for example, of a dominant male adopting an orphaned infant female which was not only underweight but had running sores around her eyes and a skin disease that had eaten away her scalp and exposed her skull. But the male gave generously of his protection and gave her a chance for life, allowing her to walk with him in the sheltered part of the troop and to sleep by his side at night.

Ineffectual as a single baboon may be against even some of the smallest of predators, several adult males acting together make formidable adversaries, as the photographs on the right suggest. It is no exaggeration to say that the males very often succeed in driving off carnivores as fierce as leopards and cheetahs with little more than threatening gestures.

CROUCHING TENSELY, adult males mistake a stuffed leopard, placed on a log to test their reactions (*top*), for the real thing. In the photograph at the bottom, after a baboon lunged at it and knocked it down, they gather around the dummy, ready to rip into it, while a female screams from a perch on a branch.

COMMANDS THEIR FULL RESPECT—THE LION. THEY FEAR IT NOT ONLY BECAUSE OF ITS SIZE AND STRENGTH BUT BECAUSE IT HUNTS IN GROUPS.

7

Clues to
Human Behaviour

IT is hardly necessary to point out that man occupies a unique position among the primates. He alone lives entirely on the ground, needing no contact with the trees to feed in, to sleep in or to take refuge from his enemies. He alone relies on weapons for defence, can use complex tools and develop an elaborate culture. He alone systematically contemplates the past and broods over the future, speculates and plans and talks, and thinks in abstractions: perceives himself as an individual possessed of a sense of good and evil, right and wrong, progress and decline.

As man does differ so widely from all the other primates, any evolutionist who is concerned with tracing the long and complex story of human development might be inclined to echo Alexander Pope's famous line: "The proper study of mankind is man". Surely one could expect to learn little from monkeys or apes about man's separate and individual evolutionary history. Yet, curiously enough, this is not the case. Just as the preliminary drawings of an artist can help an art lover to discern the genesis of the finished oil, so have the field studies of monkeys and apes in the last few decades helped anthropologists to a clearer understanding of some of the most significant aspects of man's history.

Consider, for example, one of the most decisive steps in human evolution: the descent of man's ape-like ancestors out of the trees. Why did they come down to the ground? What was the reward so great that it lured them out of their arboreal refuge? Until very recently, no one had a satisfactory answer. Now, however, we can understand what may well have happened by projecting from the monkeys which remain today in the environment that man's ape ancestors must have occupied several million years ago.

One can best begin this comparative study with the vervet, one of the most numerous non-human primates in Africa. Although vervets are still tree-dwelling monkeys, they also spend a good deal of time on the ground, and one can, with some confidence, describe the process by which they gradually, stage by stage, made their descent from the trees. As tree-dwellers, vervets fed—and still do—on fruits and seeds and leaves: all objects which often fall to the ground. At some point, vervets must have begun to go down after them. Then, once on the ground, they proceeded to move farther and farther away from the bases of the trees, moving out into the open to eat the grasses and insects they found there, until they finally reached their present stage of moving freely between one patch of trees and another.

The fact that they feed not only in trees but also under trees and between trees is certainly a principal factor in the vervets' evolutionary success. Still, they remain at least 50 per cent arboreal. To trace the next stage in the evolutionary progress of man's ancestors, it is therefore necessary to move on to the monkeys, notably the baboons and macaques, which have adapted far more thoroughly to terrestrial life.

Why these monkeys should have taken this further step it is impossible to say. Monkey fossils are rare and there are no records of baboons or macaques in the transitional stages to offer us any clues. Probably the best explanation is that they were equipped with digestive systems which enabled them to handle an exceedingly varied diet. In East Africa, for example, baboons have been known to feed off at least 200 different kinds of plants. The ability to digest so many ground plants was no doubt acquired after they descended from the trees, but the potential must have been there while they were still arboreal monkeys. Given that potential, they presumably found by experience that the greater variety of edible material there was to be found on the forest floor more than balanced the risks of settling there.

THE DOG-HEADED MAN

Early attempts by natural historians to draw primates are full of comical mistakes, more often than not introduced by the too-lively imagination of the artist. A good example is the cynocephalus, the so-called dog-headed man, taken from a natural history book printed in 1642. Long thought to be an attempt to reproduce a baboon, this creature is now suspected to have been based on early accounts of a rare Madagascar lemur, the indri. This animal often stands erect, has a long furry coat, a muzzle and very large hands. Furthermore, its tail is so short that it is often not visible.

BABOONS and macaques—and also gorillas—survived on the ground because the males acquired the long canines and other fighting characteristics that enabled them to fight off predators. When man's ape ancestors came down from the trees, they must have relied on the same type of defensive equipment. Then gradually their behaviour changed. Instead of using their teeth to defend themselves against predators, they took to using weapons, and this shift, too, is anticipated by the behaviour of certain non-human primates.

We are so used to the idea of weapons that we take them completely for granted. Actually, the use of weapons was not only a revolutionary step forward in the history of man, but it also takes quite a lot of explaining. For example, if an animal's normal method of defence is to flee from a predator, it flees. If its normal method of defence is to fight with its teeth, it fights with its teeth. It does not suddenly adopt a totally new course of action, such as picking up a stick or a rock and throwing it. The idea would simply not occur to it and, even if it did, the animal would have no reason to suppose that it would work.

Still, man's ancestors did shift from using their teeth to using weapons, and the most convincing explanation of how the shift may have taken place is one that has been suggested by the English psychologist K.R.L. Hall. As he has pointed out, orangs and various other monkeys and apes often throw down branches at other animals as an expression of hostility. Significantly, chimpanzees, the non-human primates which are in so many ways the closest to man, also throw rocks. Jane Goodall has described how she once saw a chimpanzee throwing rocks towards a photographer whose presence was keeping it from approaching a box of bananas. On other occasions, she watched chimpanzees hurling rocks, both underarm and overarm, at baboons that were competing with them for food.

Man's ape-like ancestors, no doubt, also threw branches and rocks at their enemies and, very often, the weapons they hurled must have landed on their targets and sent potential aggressors into rapid retreat. Gradually the idea must have penetrated that throwing rocks at a predator could scare it away and that it was much safer than getting into a tooth and claw fight. One favourable experience must have followed another until finally, benefiting from what they had learned, men came to use weapons regularly first to defend themselves, then later to attack animals.

TOOL-USING CHIMPANZEES

Poking a twig into a termite mound, a chimpanzee hunts for its favourite food. The insects will bite the straw, clinging to it as the ape carefully pulls it out and licks off the tasty mouthful. Observing chimpanzees in the wild, the zoologist Jane Goodall has discovered that some of them actually make termite-catching tools out of twigs, vines and stalks of grass, stripping off the leaves to produce slender stems 6 to 12 inches long. As a tool becomes bent with use, the chimpanzee will keep breaking off the damaged end until the stick is too short for probing and the ape must find a new one.

WEAPONS, of course, are simply a form of tool. For many years it has been fashionable for anthropologists to maintain that the use of tools is an essential constituent of human behaviour: that animals can only be considered human if they do make use of tools. There is much truth in this contention. To shift from reliance on one's own hands and teeth to reliance on some external instrument is a great step forward and, as we shall see in the next chapter, the use of tools was an essential step in the evolution of man.

Yet this step forward, too—as, once again, Jane Goodall has discovered—is anticipated in chimpanzees. They will strip leaves from a twig and use them to clean their bodies, to wipe off mud or to remove honey that has been smeared over bananas. They also chew leaves briefly to crumple them, and then dip them into water when they are thirsty and want to drink. Checking this behaviour, Miss Goodall found that she could draw seven or eight times as much water out of a glass by dipping crumpled leaves into it than she could by just dipping in the fingers of one hand.

The chimpanzees she observed also use tools in a more complex way by picking up twigs, grass stalks or vines, and pushing them into termite holes to draw out the insects. These tools are sometimes carefully selected. Chimpanzees may examine and reject several tangles of vines before picking one, and have been known to carry a stalk as much as a hundred feet to a termite hole. Indeed, Miss Goodall saw one male carry a stalk in its mouth for half a mile while it examined six termite holes, none of them ready for probing. The tools, once they are selected, may be prepared with considerable care, the chimpanzees often stripping the leaves from the stem with their hands or their lips. Occasionally, if a piece of grass is too wide to go into a termite hole, a chimpanzee may make it fit by pulling long strips from it.

Once the tool is prepared and the termite hole located, the chimpanzee scrapes away the thin layer of soil which seals it up. Then it pokes the vine or stalk inside and withdraws it, covered with termites, which the chimpanzee then licks off with its lips.

This kind of planning ahead is of peculiar interest because the ability to visualize a situation before it exists is often cited as a principal factor distinguishing man from all other animals. At first glance, the behaviour of the chimpanzees appears to refute this assumption. But is a tool-using chimpanzee really thinking ahead, imagining a situation that does not yet exist? Not perhaps in the way a man does when he fashions a bow for the hunt. The man is preparing to kill an animal he has not yet seen, while the chimpanzee seems simply to be reacting to the stimulus of the termite nests, just as a Galápagos woodpecker-finch reacts to the presence of insects by probing for them with a cactus spine or a twig held in its beak, or as a sea otter reacts to molluscs by breaking their shells open with a stone.

To early man, tools were particularly useful because they enabled him, in time, to widen the sources of his food supply—to kill not only small but increasingly larger animals. In short, tools made it possible for man to become a predator—and for a long time this was thought to be one of the qualities which distinguished early man from the non-human primates, since these, except for the eating of insects, were generally assumed to be vegetarians.

But is the distinction quite that absolute between man, the hunter of animals and eater of meat, and all the other primates? We know now, on the basis of a great deal of information gathered during the past decades, that it is not. Observations in the wild have shown that both baboons and chimpanzees do, on occasion, prey on weaker animals for food. The behaviour of baboons as meat-eaters is particularly interesting because it appears to vary with the experience of the group involved. All baboons so far observed will eat eggs, fledgling birds, or small animals that they happen to stumble across in the grass. Beyond that, however, the behaviour of different groups seems to vary. Some will mingle quite peacefully with guinea fowl; others will kill and eat them. Some baboons will deliberately chase, kill and eat hares, young gazelles or even vervet monkeys. One baboon, indeed, was seen to chase a young hare for more than 70 yards before catching it. And yet others may actually grip an edible animal in their mouths, only to release it, as a female baboon was once seen to do. She caught a vervet, held it in her jaws and then, apparently bewildered by the situation, let the smaller monkey go free.

WHY all the variations? The answer seems to lie in group tradition. Possibly, among one group, a tradition of meat-eating will arise by accident. A baboon will find a hare or a vervet, will kill it and eat it. The same thing will happen again and again, until finally the whole group will begin to chase animals for food. Predation will become part of the group's general behaviour, will be taken up by other neighbouring groups, and will be passed down to later generations. Among other groups of baboons, however, living in different areas, such a tradition for various reasons may not develop. Possibly the original fortuitous catches did not occur in sufficient numbers for a new tradition to become established; or possibly the non-predatory baboons lived in areas where there was enough vegetable food available to satisfy their needs, so that they never acquired the drive to catch and eat animals.

Chimpanzees, too, can be predators. They kill and eat young bush-buck and bush-pig, and can prey, at least occasionally, on monkeys.

"The prey," as Jane Goodall has described one such incident, "a red colobus monkey, was sitting in a tree when an adolescent male chimpanzee climbed a neighbouring tree and remained very still as the monkey looked towards it. A second adolescent male chimpanzee then climbed the tree in which the colobus was sitting, ran quickly along the branch, leapt at the colobus, and caught it with its hands, presumably breaking its neck, as it did not struggle or call out." As soon as the colobus had been killed, other chimpanzees jumped up into the tree to share in the spoils. This killing and the reactions of the other chimpanzees certainly bear all the marks of deliberate hunting.

In another way, also, the behaviour of chimpanzees appears to anticipate the evolution of human attitudes towards meat and hunting. When an adult male chimpanzee is in possession of some meat, the other members of the group will sit around, holding out their hands as if begging for a share. This kind of begging and sharing has never been observed in other non-human primates, nor among chimpanzees except when one was holding food. Inevitably, one is reminded of the situation which came about when men became hunters and the females and young in the group were only able to obtain meat if it was handed to them by the adult males who had caught it.

THE comparison with man must not be pushed too far. Essentially, chimpanzees are not predators and meat forms a very minor part of their diet, as it does with baboons. None the less, one may speculate that the predatory behaviour of chimpanzees and baboons does offer a clue to the origins of organized hunting, the practice which, as will be seen in the following chapter, played an absolutely central role in the history of human development. At first, perhaps through a series of accidental killings, a few groups of early men may have been spurred on to become hunters. Then, gradually, the habit must have spread. As man refined his tools, hunting must have become progressively easier and must have consumed more and more time until finally it became a fundamental part of human behaviour.

In yet another and quite unrelated form of activity generally considered unique to humans, some monkeys and apes do definitely anticipate human behaviour. Only with difficulty can one imagine a monkey or an ape playing the role of artist. Yet it is undeniable that some of them can and do paint. Capuchin monkeys, orangs and at least one gorilla have been successfully coaxed into trying their hand with the brush, and chimpanzees, as is so often the case, have proved particularly co-operative.

The results have been intriguing, even startling, for apparently chimpanzees paint very much as a human child does. This, at least, is the contention advanced by an English zoologist, Desmond Morris, who observed the work of a young male chimpanzee, Congo, for more than two years, and has described his findings in a fascinating book, *The Biology of Art*. Congo began to paint at the age of one-and-a-half, using at first a primitive, clutching grip, and then progressing to a more delicate one with the brush held between his thumb and forefinger. Shortly before he lost interest in painting, Congo was drawing circles and making marks inside them, which is the stage a human child normally passes through just before he begins to draw faces.

But the really significant point of Morris's study was his demonstration that a chimpanzee does not paint at random. It possesses a definite and discernible sense of form and even an individual style. As Sir Julian Huxley has declared, chimpanzees are obviously endowed with artistic potentialities that can be brought to light if a suitable opportunity is provided, and these potentialities may perhaps be interpreted as a first step along the long road that led ultimately to human art.

The chimpanzees' attitude to painting also offers some intriguing opportunities for comparison of their emotional make-up with that of human children—on, for example, the kind of psychological disturbances that might afflict them. When the works of a one-year-old female, Beth, and a three-year-old male, Dr. Tom, were shown to psychologists trained in the study of children's painting, the psychologists interpreted Dr. Tom's work as that of an aggressive seven- or eight-year-old boy with paranoid tendencies, and that of Beth as the work of a fiercely belligerent ten-year-old girl of the schizoid type.

It is tempting to claim that these interpretations revealed more about the psychologists than they did about the chimpanzees, but to do so would be unfair. Young chimpanzees are much more advanced physically than human children of the same age. Furthermore, the two animals tested were not only under the normal tensions of captivity but had been appearing every week on television; as Morris comments, they may well have developed aberrant tendencies. Besides, the psychologists were none too far from the truth—or from *a* truth. For captive chimpanzees can be more belligerent and paranoid than the average human. Individuals vary, of course. Some are timid, some bold. Some are often altruistic, others are bullies. Still, a few generalizations can be offered. When young, although playful, energetic and appreciative of favours, they can also show many of the qualities of a fractious and unpleasant child, especially in temper tantrums.

THE brain of a human child, is, of course, very different from that of a young ape or monkey. A human child possesses a vastly more complex brain which greatly increases its capacity to learn, to acquire knowledge and develop skills. Yet the study of non-human primates can also offer some valuable insights into the operations of the human intelligence—for example, into the way human beings learn, and learn how to learn.

How does a child learn to solve algebraic equations? Or to use language correctly? Or, to pose the same issue in social terms, how does a good salesman learn to perceive, as if by instinct, the right approach to use on a potential customer? For several hundred years, it was widely believed that while some knowledge is acquired through the process of trial and error, the great mass is accumulated through a succession of sudden flashes of insight. Actually, these assumptions were mere armchair theorizing, for there was no way to put them to the test. One cannot keep a human being in a laboratory in order to trace the development of his learning processes. But, as Harry Harlow of the University of Wisconsin has demonstrated, one can do exactly that with monkeys. Very skilfully, Harlow explored a new method of testing primate psychology. Instead of basing his tests on his monkeys' ability to manipulate objects—i.e., to solve single problems—he based them on the monkeys' ability to discriminate between objects of varying shapes and colours in a variety of situations. This ability, which in primates is not innate but must be learned, is absolutely vital to a monkey: it is only through its powers of discrimination that it can pick out food from the surrounding mass of inedible objects. One can therefore assume that the way a monkey learns to discriminate fairly reflects the general pattern of his learning processes.

Harlow began his experiments by putting two objects of different shapes, colours and sizes in front of his monkeys, with a food reward concealed under one of them. After a series of trials and mistakes, the monkeys learned to pick out the right object every time. Then Harlow moved on to confront them with three objects, one of which was different from the others. Once again, after a series of trials and mistakes, the monkeys learned always or nearly always to pick out the object that was unlike the others. Gradually, progressing from one stage of complexity to the next, Harlow kept making his problems more difficult until finally his monkeys were performing, practically without a mistake, feats that required considerable powers of thought. Confronted with three objects on an orange-coloured tray, they would regularly pick out the one that was different in shape from the others. Confronted with the same objects on a cream-coloured tray, they picked out the one that was unique in colour.

The monkeys were able to progress because, at each new stage of complexity, they mastered some new principle of selection. Once it was mastered, they were then able to apply it to every similar problem and also to remember it for a year or more. Item by item, the monkeys built up a store of knowledge, just as a child does when it learns how to conjugate different tenses of verbs or understand progressively more difficult geometric theorems.

In Harlow's phrase, the monkeys acquired "learning sets", each one an organized set of habits that enabled them to solve any problem of a particular type. As the sets accumulated, the monkeys' patterns of thinking grew steadily more complex. Projecting from monkeys to humans, Harlow concluded that people learn in the same way. From early childhood on, they are continually attempting to solve problems, making mistakes, and drawing the appropriate conclusions as to what will work and what will not. This means that all our knowledge is founded on immensely complicated assemblages of learning sets. The diver going off a high-board, the poker-player betting on a pair, the would-be lover holding off his advances to provoke a girl's curiosity . . . all of them are acting, whether they are aware of it or not, on the basis of an enormously complex mass of habits and patterns of behaviour that have been tested in the past and found to be effective. "Experience never teaches", is the frequently heard cry of the despairing sceptic. But if Harlow is correct, and the concept of learning through sudden flashes of innate insight is false, then experience, however often neglected, proves after all to be the only teacher we possess.

THE study of non-human primates can also yield some extremely useful insight into another aspect of the human brain—into the causes of human neuroses. The reader will perhaps remember a reference made earlier in this book to Harlow's discovery that some of his infant monkeys displayed types of neurotic behaviour that were strikingly similar to those observed in humans. In fact the patterns of neuroses a monkey can suffer read rather like a list of entries in a psychiatrist's notebook: inability to live a normal social life, aberrant sexual activity, incompetent—even abusive—maternal conduct, the juvenile-delinquent syndrome. These and other forms of abnormal behaviour have been observed in monkeys, and all of them are the consequence of either inadequate mothering or isolation from other infants.

But how long must a monkey be kept in isolation before its neuroses become so deeply implanted that they can never be eradicated? The answer is both relevant to the human condition and, potentially, of considerable value to people engaged in trying to salvage children from the consequences of infancy without affection. Through another series of classic experiments, Harlow was able to pin-point the period with considerable accuracy. He found that if an infant macaque is kept in isolation for some 60 to 90 days after its birth and is then allowed to mix with other monkeys, its neurotic tendencies can be corrected and it will grow up quite normal. But every added week beyond that time reduces

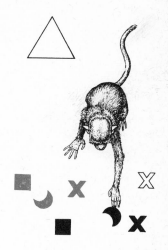

THE THINKING RHESUS

Can a monkey think? Certainly, as these experiments with a rhesus by Benjamin Weinstein demonstrate. First he conditioned the monkey to react to colour by teaching it to push forward black objects when shown a black triangle, and brown objects when shown a brown circle. Then Weinstein went on to the more difficult step of presenting an uncoloured triangle and circle (drawings above and below). The monkey was still able to select the appropriate colours, proving it had mastered the sophisticated mental step of linking up a shape with a colour.

the chance that the monkey can ever recover from the baleful effects of its early deprivation.

A rhesus monkey, it should be remembered, is more advanced at birth than a human infant, and it matures four times as rapidly. The critical period in the development of humans, therefore, occurs later, but since laboratory experiments cannot be performed on human infants, the exactly comparable ages are not known. Probably the first six months of human life correspond roughly to the first week or two in the life of a monkey; for both, this is the time when the most important factor is simple survival with the help of adequate food, warmth and care. But from then on, for the next two or three years, it is likely that man, with his larger brain and learning capacity, is more susceptible to his environment than the monkey. If a child is deprived during this time of affection, companionship and opportunities to learn the things it needs to know for successful living, the effects on both its temperament and intelligence may be almost permanent. Such, in any event, is the suggestion derived from experiments like Harlow's; but the results of any such work would have to be checked on humans themselves if we are to be sure.

Experimenting in his laboratory with rhesus monkeys, Harlow also came to a number of tentative conclusions about motherhood which may bear on human behaviour. Why are some mothers attentive and loving, others indifferent or even brutal? Is it a question of genetic make-up? No doubt, up to a point. As Phyllis Jay has observed, some monkey females are better mothers than others. Monkeys, like humans, are not all born with equal talents. Still, monkey mothers so far observed in the wild have been generally attentive to their offspring at least during the first weeks of their lives. One might be tempted to credit this to the natural instinct of motherhood, but to do so would be only a half-truth, because the popular concept of instinct is far from accurate. Actually monkeys—and men and women—are born possessed only of emotional "tendencies", and those tendencies will flower into action only if their possessor enjoys the appropriate experiences.

If she is to grow up to be a good mother, a female monkey must, among other normal experiences, herself receive proper maternal care—or so Harlow concluded from a study of four monkey females which had been raised in isolation without real mothers. When they in their turn became mothers, they displayed none of the attentiveness that a monkey female in the wild lavishes on her offspring. They were reluctant to feed their infants. They seemed not to care when the infants were taken from them by keepers, and some treated their infants with positive cruelty. If one can, in fact, legitimately project from monkeys to humans, then the conclusion is obvious: human females must enjoy the attentions of a loving mother if they are to give their own children the love and attention that every child needs.

And what happens to the offspring, both male and female, of such unloving mothers? Very much the same as what happens to human children who are raised without affection. The infants of Harlow's "motherless mothers" turned out to be aggressive in temper and precocious in their sexual behaviour, two characteristics that have been found to be among the most common marks of the disturbed child. Far-fetched as it may seem, when one considers how vast a gap separates the non-human primates from human beings, monkeys bear in themselves many of the emotional qualities, both normal and abnormal, of that unique creature—man.

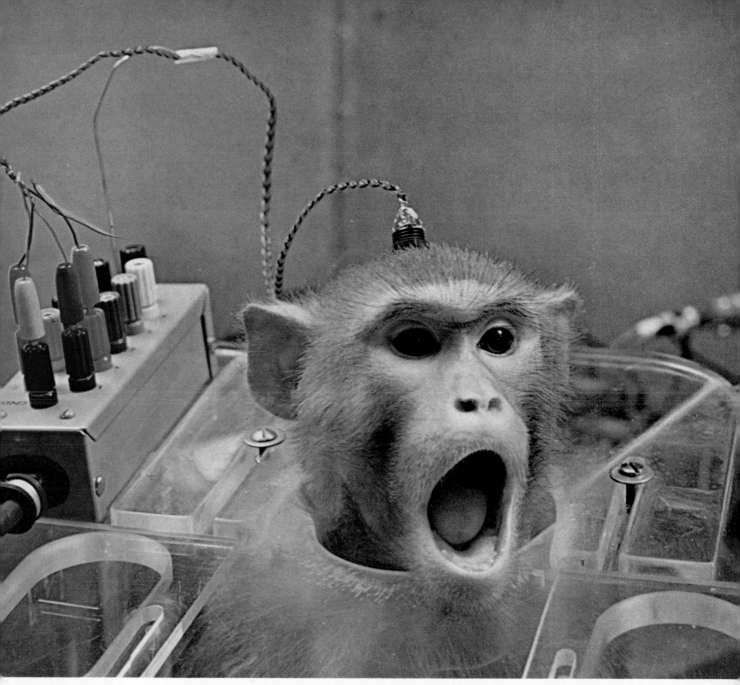

OBLIVIOUS TO ELECTRODES MEASURING ITS BRAIN ACTIVITY, THIS RHESUS MONKEY REACTS TO THE PHOTOGRAPHER WITH A TYPICAL THREAT.

Science and the Primate

Because of their physical and emotional similarities to man, primates are invaluable substitutes in scientific research. Without them, many medical discoveries would never have been made, and the first astronauts would have faced far greater risks. While always subject to some controversy, such research today is conducted with scrupulous care, and its achievements are unquestionable.

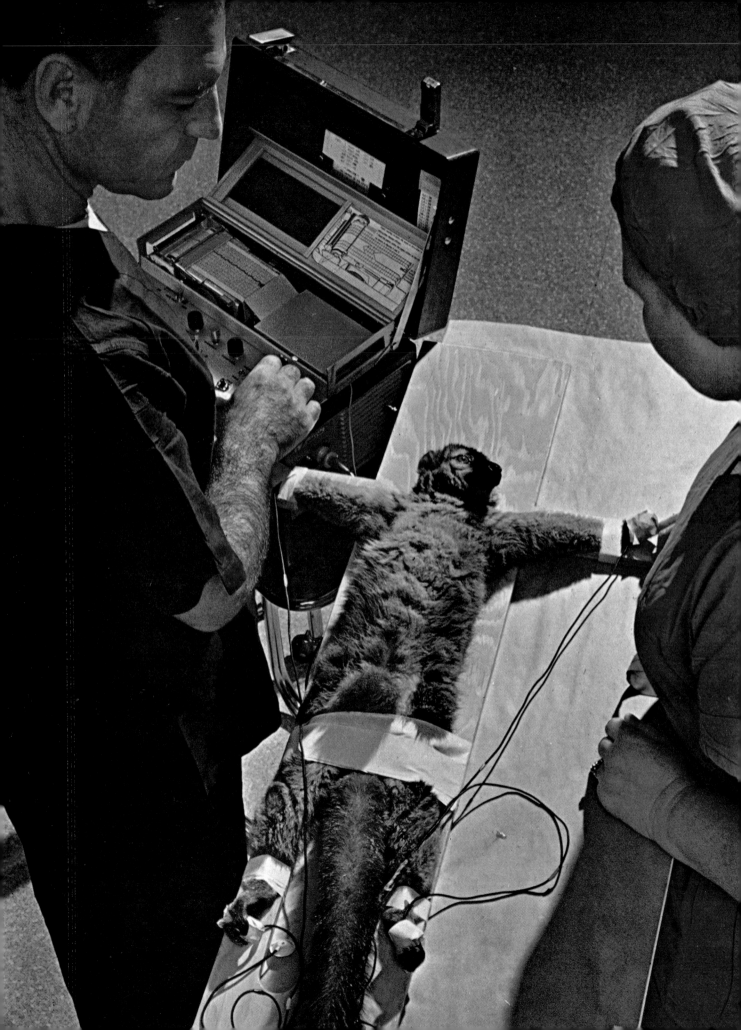

A New Age of Research

From primate research have come some of the most important advances in modern medical history. Research on rhesus monkeys, for example, was responsible for the discovery of the vital Rh factor—named after them—in red blood cells. This gave rise to entirely new knowledge of blood transfusions and, by matching people of similar Rh blood, saved thousands of human lives which otherwise would have been lost. Today the most significant research is in the field of transplants, to the end that defective human kidneys and hearts may eventually be replaced by healthy organs from apes and monkeys.

There are now seven primate centres in the U.S. Each, like the Oregon laboratory shown on this page, gives its animals the best possible care, not only for humane reasons but also because primates represent a big investment: rhesus monkeys cost about £20 each, a baby chimp is worth nearly £300 and young orang-outangs cost nearly £2,000.

THE CELEBES APE is actually a monkey and seems to have a more tractable disposition than the rhesus. Increasingly bred for laboratory use, it may replace the temperamental rhesus.

AN ELECTROCARDIOGRAM is performed on a lemur at Beaverton, Oregon, to provide norms for testing body functions. This was the first centre to work extensively with prosimians.

OUTDOOR CAGES provide plentiful sun and shade for the primates at the Oregon centre. One of eight such buildings, this breeding compound houses one male and dozens of females.

161

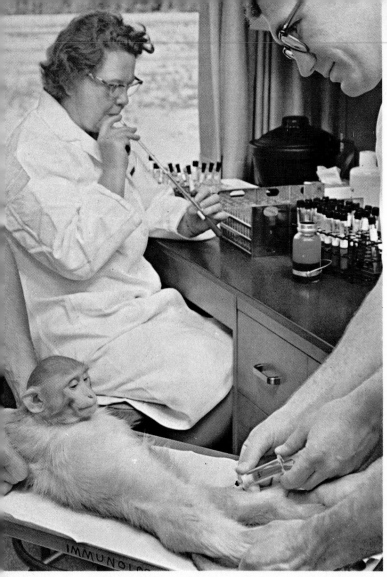

GIVING BLOOD, a monkey watches as a sample is drawn from its leg. The blood is examined by Dr. Marjorie LaSalle, who is studying primate tissue transplants and blood transfusions.

The Primate's Role in Medicine

The medical research being conducted on primates at the Oregon centre is aimed at gaining knowledge—basic facts that may lead to the banishment of some of man's most serious diseases and disorders. The many areas being investigated include muscular dystrophy, skin disorders, the effects of hormones during and after pregnancy, the electrical behaviour of the brain, heart disease, atherosclerosis and the relationship between viruses and cancer. Data from the daily examinations of the 1,000 primates at the centre are compiled by a computer, one of the first attempts to employ modern computer techniques in medical record-keeping. Similar procedures, applied to human hospital records, are expediting tedious paper work involved in hospital management.

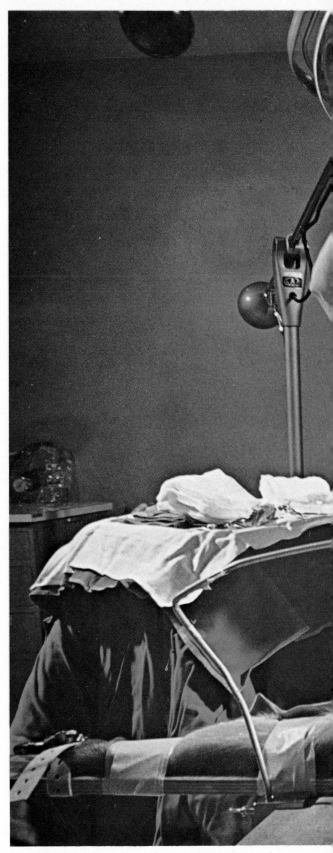

IN SURGERY, a fully anaesthetized rhesus monkey undergoes a cardiac catheterization—a delicate operation in which a thin tube is threaded through its femoral vein into its heart. Sur-

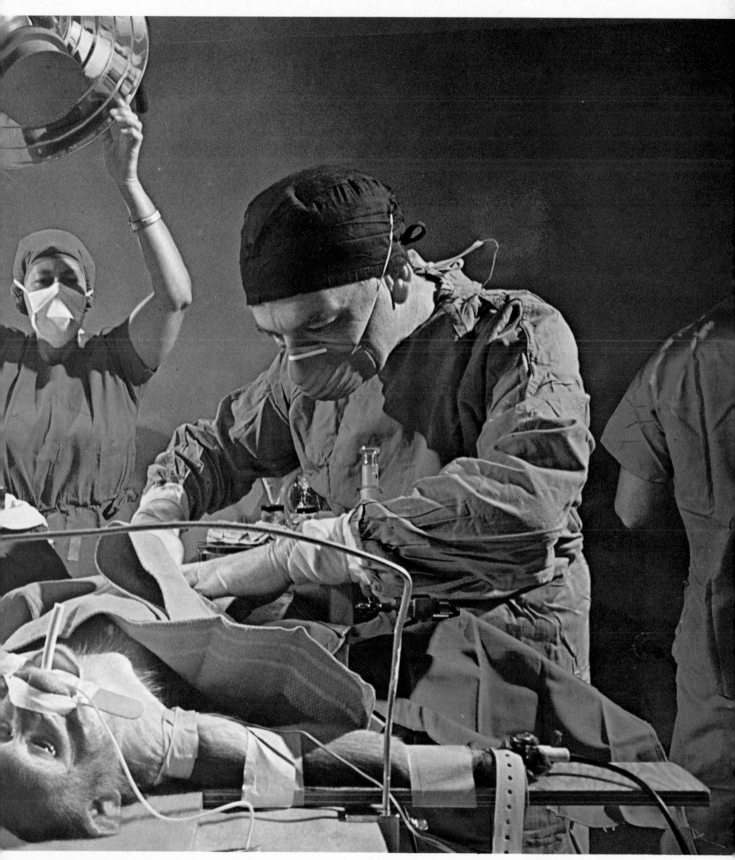

geon René Malinow collects blood from within the animal's heart for analysis. Directing the light in the background is a registered nurse. The tongue depressor keeps the monkey from choking, and the tube in its mouth prevents mucus from collecting in its throat—all precautions that are meticulously observed in similar operations performed on human patients.

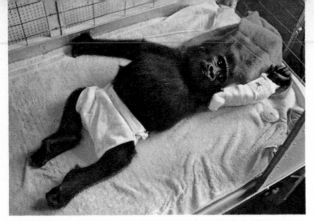

A VICTIM OF POLIO, this baby gorilla is improving after extensive physiotherapy. The disease was not induced; as with tuberculosis and hepatitis, apes are as susceptible to it as man.

A Laboratory for Behaviour

While medical research has been emphasized at the Oregon centre, the Yerkes Regional Primate Center in Atlanta, Georgia, is devoted to behavioural studies as well. Chimpanzees, orang-outangs and gorillas here are undergoing tests to explore their intellectual processes, personality traits and social behaviour. Pigtail macaques are being studied to determine the most important factors in the establishment of

a social hierarchy, and extensive experiments are being conducted into the nature of alcoholism and drug addiction.

The Yerkes centre was started in 1930 in Orange Park, Florida, with a total primate population of 25 chimpanzees. Today it has the largest collection of apes in the U.S.: 71 chimpanzees, 28 orangoutangs and 9 gorillas, as well as more than 100 monkeys of various species. Although psychobiology is still a major part of the centre's programme, there is a growing volume of physiological research, including studies on damaged muscle fibres and connective tissues. Scientists at the centre are also vitally interested in primate breeding: a self-perpetuating colony is an urgent necessity, since many species of primates in the wild are on the verge of extinction.

A HUNGRY ORANG picks the red cross and earns a piece of fruit in a test for shape and colour discrimination. Having eaten (*bottom*), however, a subject often becomes satiated and quits.

A BIBULOUS CHIMP savours its daily ration of alcohol and orange juice. After six months it showed no signs of alcoholism, and could guzzle a bottle before it became visibly inebriated.

165

INFANTS PLAY in a room designed for study of infant relationships. With the toys and gymnastic equipment are two artificial mothers that give solace when an infant becomes anxious.

Studies in Monkey Love

What is the nature of primate affection? Are the emotions that a monkey or ape experiences comparable to that peculiarly human emotion called love? To answer these questions, Dr. Harry Harlow of the Wisconsin Regional Primate Center launched a full-scale study of infant rhesus monkeys and the factors that influence their behaviour towards each other. After a decade of tests and observations, Harlow arrived at the conclusion that primates experience affection in five distinct ways, each classified

TERROR ENTERS in the form of a drum-beating Teddy bear. This was a test to determine whether a terrified infant would seek security in an inanimate mother.

THE INFANT FLEES from the advancing drummer, seeking its cloth mother. The wire mother to the right was rejected by virtually every one of the frightened infants.

as a separate and distinct "affectional system". These systems include the love expressed by an infant towards its mother, the affection that an adult male feels for infants, the camaraderie that exists between a juvenile and its contemporaries, the affection of a mother for her own offspring, and the sexual attraction between adults or juveniles of opposite sexes. Of all the different kinds of love, the most basic is the first—an infant's complete dependence upon its mother. Harlow has amply dem-onstrated the power of these kinds of affection with a number of different experiments, notably those involving infants' relationships to wire or terry cloth mothers. In a study of an infant's response to fright (*below*), Harlow started with the general observation that young primates of any species, including human beings, usually seek the protection of their mothers during times of danger or stress. This series of experiments proved that brief contact with a cloth mother served admirably as an antidote to fear.

REASSURED by the soft warmth of its cloth mother, the infant peers at the fearsome intruder. Several of the infants regained enough confidence to leave the mother and go to investigate.

IN SOUTHERN INDIA, anthropologist Phyllis Jay confers with a team of Japanese scientists. They spent years pioneering in studies of macaques and langurs in their native environment.

IN AFRICA, Irven DeVore, co-author of this book, took some 45,000 feet of colour film to record in fascinating detail the intricate structure and inter-relationships of a baboon society.

IN CEYLON, Suzanne Ripley poses with her pets—baby langurs and a macaque with a penchant for grooming hair. She spent 15 months in the jungle with only two native assistants.

IN THE CARIBBEAN, a rhesus macaque adopts a threat posture in a monkey colony near Puerto Rico. The "72" tattoo identifies it for records.

Revelations in the Field

Not until 1931, when C. R. Carpenter journeyed to Panama to study howler monkeys, had a scientist actually gone out into the field to observe primates systematically in their own environments. He published some revolutionary findings on monkey behaviour which pointed to the fallacy of studying captive species; despite this, no further extensive field research was undertaken until after World War II. Then, with the establishment of the Primate Research Group in Japan where monkeys began to be meticulously studied under natural conditions, an entirely new concept of primate research unfolded. Today, scores of specialized experts from several countries are teaming up to study primate behaviour in the wild. Such interdisciplinary field research has already produced more fully rounded pictures than man has ever had before of his primate cousins.

IN BORNEO, Barbara Harrisson hauls a struggling proboscis monkey from the water. She patiently rehabilitates lost or homeless monkeys and apes so that they can return to normal lives in the jungle.

What Can Be Learned from Primate Art

In the half-century that apes and monkeys have been painting, some of their work has been seriously studied, but much of it has been used in elaborate practical jokes. For instance, paintings by the chimpanzee Pierre in Sweden (*opposite*) were displayed in 1964 under the name Pierre Brassau. His works were given serious critical comment, and several were sold before the hoax was discovered.

That there is a valid purpose in studying primate art, however, is the contention of zoologist Desmond Morris, whose chimpanzee Congo painted the pictures below. According to Morris, primate art pro-

A FINGER PAINTING shows Congo's favourite design—a radiating pattern. Most of his paintings were done with a brush; with finger paints he tended to obliterate his original design.

HEAVY HORIZONTAL LINES embellish Congo's more usual fan pattern. Sometimes he stumbled upon new techniques, such as scratching the picture with his finger-nails or even licking it.

A CENTRAL DOT surrounded by swaths of colour suggests at least an elementary grasp of composition. Further evidence is that Congo almost always painted within the paper's borders.

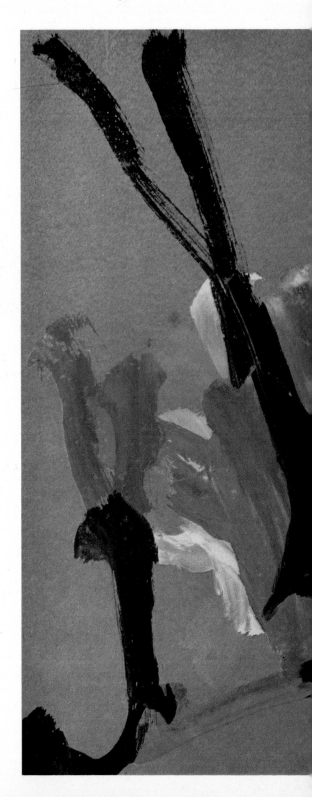

vides a source of basic artistic expression that may reveal the origins of human art. Thus, chimpanzees exhibit a rudimentary sense of composition, and also, apparently, they have an urge of some sort which is satisfied by painting: Congo painted avidly for three years without ever having to be enticed.

A CELEBRATED ARTIST, a chimp named Pierre sits at an easel in a Swedish zoo and chooses colours from a palette. Very highstrung, Pierre often eats a banana a minute while he paints.

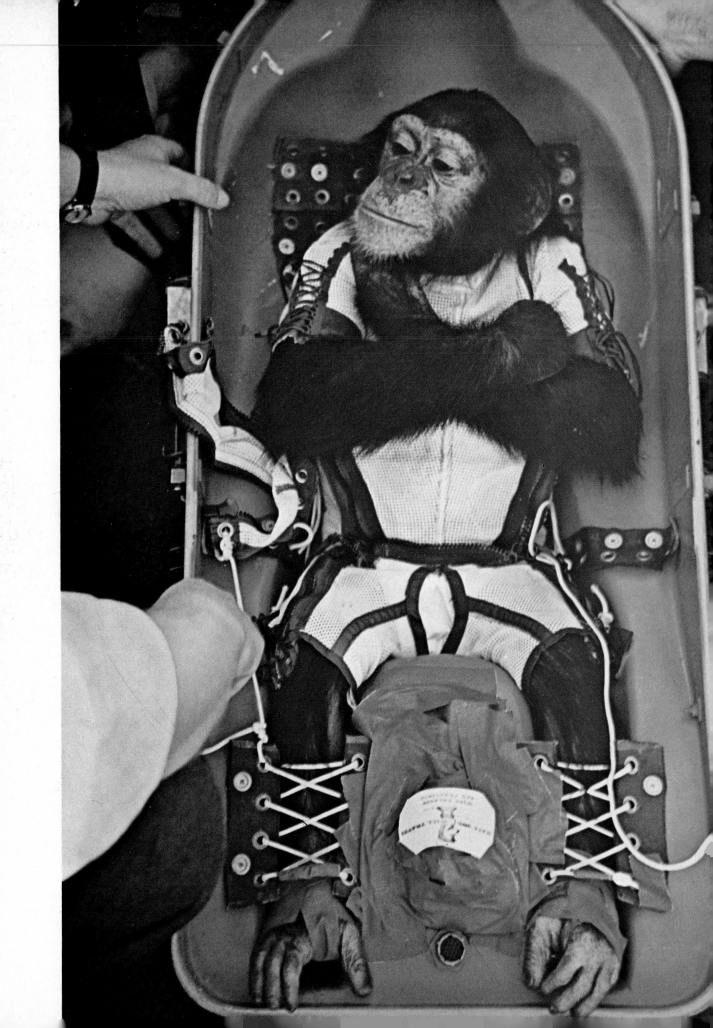

Understudies for Man in the Conquest of Space

When the successful development of rock-
ets in the late 1940's made the exploration of space a workable reality, animals
were the first to be sent out into this unknown realm. The first "astronauts" were
fungus spores and fruit-flies launched
from Holloman Air Force Base in New
Mexico. In 1949, a rhesus monkey survived a trip 83 miles high; subsequent
tests culminated in the 1961 suborbital
flight of the chimpanzee Ham (*left*).

One of the numerous questions which
test animals helped to answer before man
could embark on an extended space jour-
ney was what he should breathe. The
first tests indicated that pure oxygen
at about one-third normal atmospheric
pressure could safely be used for the Mer-
cury flights. Now, however, with greatly
extended flights in prospect, some scientists fear that pure oxygen might be harmful over a long period. Thus, tests like
the one with the macaque monkey named
Lizzie (*right*) are being conducted in an
effort to find a new mixture of gases that
an astronaut on a long interplanetary
flight could breathe with no ill effects.

BREATHING PURE OXYGEN in a test
for possible toxic effects, this macaque was safely sealed for 90 days
in this chamber. It exercised by
having to pull a lever 80 times for
a single portion of food or water.

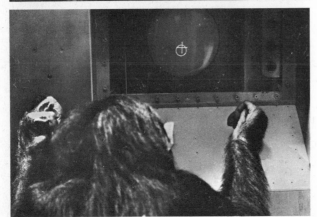

Preparing for a Low-Pressure Life

One of the most important projects at Holloman Air Force Base is the investigation of atmospheric pressure and its effects upon the mind and body. Chimpanzees are taught under normal conditions to perform routine tasks (*left and below*). Then they are tested in extreme conditions of cold, heat, weightlessness—even partial vacuums—giving scientists valuable insights into the effects of different stresses. One danger that astronauts constantly face is the possibility of being plunged into a total vacuum by a sudden leak. Chimpanzees like the one shown opposite have been subjected to total vacuums for more than two minutes and have survived. One inflated like a balloon—its heart, respiration and electrical brain activity stopped, but about an hour after normal pressure was restored, it had completely recovered and was performing all its assigned tasks.

A WELL-TRAINED CHIMP manœuvres a drifting circle directly over a stationary cross by moving a lever. It collects a banana pellet as a reward (*third picture*) and then starts all over again.

A NOUGHTS AND CROSSES PLAYER, this chimpanzee has mastered the game and often beats the experimenter. It lights up the circles or Xs by touching the squares in front of it.

DAZED BUT RECOVERING, A CHIMP IS BROUGHT BACK TO SEA-LEVEL PRESSURE AFTER UNDERGOING TOTAL VACUUM.

8

From Ape towards Man

SOME 15 to 20 million years ago, several different species of apes inhabited the huge forest which then stretched, unbroken by any major water barriers, from the west coast of Africa to what are now the islands of the East Indies. Then, in a slow but decisive manner, the climate changed. The forests of the Middle East dried out and were transformed into desert, and the great population of apes was split into two groups whose descendants still survive as the chimpanzee and the gorilla of Africa, and the orang and the gibbon of East Asia. But in between, over an area which covers several million square miles, no apes survive at all. What happened to them? Where did they go? These questions are of vital interest to us because it may well be that their descendants were the ancestors of man.

Unfortunately, the early stages of man's evolutionary progress along his own individual line remain a total mystery, and several million years must have elapsed before they reached the stage where we can, with some confidence, take up their story. We do know that between one-and-a-half and two million years ago at least two varieties of small ape-like men had come into existence in South and East Africa—and, no doubt, across much of southern Asia also. These intermediate creatures stood about five feet tall, one weighing about 4 stone and the other about 7 stone. Their brains were not quite as large as that of a large male gorilla. But, unlike any ape, they could run, though they probably could not yet stride, in an upright position with their bodies balanced on their hind legs.

We owe our knowledge of the Australopithecines—as these primitive, small-brained ape men were called—to the patient archaeological researches of three remarkable men. In 1924, Raymond A. Dart, a professor of anatomy at the University of Witwatersrand, noticed in a skull that had been dug up not far from Johannesburg the traces of a very early type of hominid: part ape, part man. During the next few years, Dart's discoveries were confirmed by those of more Australopithecine fossils, unearthed elsewhere in South Africa by a Scottish physician, Robert Broom, who, excited by Dart's initial find, had come out to join in the search.

Meanwhile, an English prehistorian, Louis Leakey, had also started to hunt for fossils of early men, at Olduvai Gorge in Tanganyika. For nearly 30 years, Leakey and his wife Mary kept up the hunt, digging up the fossils of ancient animals and equally ancient tools. Then, in 1959, Leakey made a great find. He unearthed the fossil remains of a creature very similar to Dart's *Australopithecus*, and he also made two other discoveries of enormous significance. Close to the fossils there were tools made out of pebbles, chipped to give them a sharp cutting edge; and there were also the bones of small animals—of rats and mice and small pigs and antelope.

These finds provided the basis for the first coherent and satisfactory explanation of how man came to evolve out of his ape-like ancestors. This evolutionary process has been stated in considerable detail by Professor Sherwood Washburn of the University of California, and much of what follows has been based upon his series of papers on the subject.

Washburn's explanation of how early man came into existence is not merely novel; it also contradicts a number of assumptions that had previously gone largely unquestioned. Long before Leakey unearthed his Australopithecine fossils in 1959, most anthropologists were agreed that the only animals that could properly be considered human were the ones that were able to make and to use tools. But how had man acquired the ability to use tools? The fashionable answer was that he had first developed a uniquely large, complex and efficient brain. Possessed of this extremely serviceable brain, he was able to manipulate tools. And he could do so the more easily because somehow he had also become a bipedal creature who could stand up and move about on two legs with his arms and hands left free.

THE reader will perhaps perceive the flaw in this interpretation of man's evolutionary progress. Animals only acquire new characteristics if they provide some immediate advantage. They are never acquired merely by accident, to be stored away, as it were, like money in the bank, possibly to serve some useful purpose in the distant future. It is therefore inconceivable that man should first have acquired a large brain—and an erect posture—for no particular purpose, and then, later, should have taken advantage of these characteristics to make and to use tools. The processes of evolution simply do not allow for such lucky strokes of fortune.

Actually, as Leakey's finds demonstrated, the traditional explanation of human evolution had placed the horse with great precision right behind the cart.

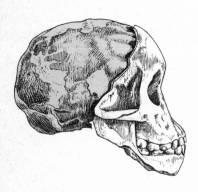

BETWEEN MAN AND APE

Australopithecus—"australis" meaning "south" and "pithecus" meaning "ape" —is the name Professor Raymond A. Dart gave to his historic discovery of a primate fossil over one million years old, taken from a quarry in South Africa in 1924. This fossil, the skull of a child about six years old, is in two pieces. One part consists of facial bones and teeth. The other (shown in colour) is a stone cast formed inside the skull, and denotes the shape and size of the brain, even though most of the brain case itself is missing. Together they give a picture of a transitional form, having somewhat human features and a brain capacity larger than that of a chimpanzee but not as large as that of the earliest true man.

Although the Australopithecines had brains little bigger than those of a chimpanzee, they had already learned to fashion and to use simple tools—probably for hunting. Later in this chapter, we shall see how man did in fact come to acquire his unique brain. For the moment, however, we shall confine ourselves to the earlier stages of his progress, as they can be deduced from what we know about non-human primates, and from the evidence of Leakey's discoveries at Olduvai.

To set man's evolutionary history in the proper perspective, it is necessary to realize that the Australopithecines whose remains have been discovered were not the earliest hominids. By way of illustration, suppose that in a few million years' time some future Dart or Leakey descends from outer space on to an earth where man no longer exists, and digs up the fossils of a few 20th-century humans. If he assumed that those humans had been among the first, he would clearly be making a grievous error, and so would anyone who assumed that the Australopithecines so far discovered were representatives of the earliest hominids.

THERE is, in fact, very good reason to suppose that they were comparative late-comers on the scene. When man's ape-like ancestors descended from the trees, they must have been exposed to attacks from predators and, like male baboons, macaques and gorillas, the male hominids almost certainly possessed long canines which they used to defend themselves, their females and their young. Had they not done so, the hominids would surely have been wiped out. Yet the Australopithecine fossils show that these little ape-like men possessed canines no longer or sharper than those of modern man. What happened to this obviously necessary defensive adaptation? Presumably they lost their long canines because they learned to use weapons instead of their teeth for defence, and this change must have taken a long time to occur.

At the same time, another enormously significant change was also taking place. When they first came to the ground, man's ape-like predecessors must have relied almost exclusively on their fingers and their teeth to obtain food. Then, gradually, they began to adapt to life on the ground in a fashion unique to themselves. They discovered the value of tools: very primitive ones at first, no doubt—perhaps no more complex than the sticks which chimpanzees use to dig out termites. The important point is, however, that these hominids did not stop there—they went on to develop tools that were much more elaborate and, in the process of doing so, they acquired fingers and thumbs suitable for the manipulation of comparatively complex instruments.

The Australopithecines possessed such manipulable fingers and thumbs, and these very useful digits must have taken a very long time to evolve. Much time, too, must have been required for the hominids to acquire the important physical characteristics that enabled the Australopithecines to move in an erect position, bipedally, with their bodies supported on their legs. How much time? Four million years, perhaps. Or six. Or eight. In the present stage of our knowledge, it is impossible to be more precise.

It was, of course, no coincidence that all these various changes—in the teeth and the fingers and thumbs, in the pelvis, and the leg and the foot—should have taken place in the same animals. For the shift to bipedalism and the use of tools, as we can logically reconstruct it now, were very closely connected. With each new shift towards bipedalism, the hominids' hands were left more free to make and to use tools. As they came to rely more on tools, they had a greater incentive to depend on their legs for support. So they experienced a further shift towards bipedalism.

In other words, the hominids evolved through a continual process of feedback, with the use of tools and their bipedal posture acting as mutual cause and effect. While the idea of evolutionary progress by feedback may seem very obvious once it has been suggested, it is in fact a radical departure from traditional thinking, and has begun to win acceptance only in the past decade. Actually, all evolutionary progress, not only that of man, has taken place through a series of very tiny changes, each one at once producing some small advantage and paving the way for the next change.

Bᴜᴛ why, to pose the obvious question, was it only the hominids who benefited from the feedback interaction between bipedalism and the use of tools? Chimpanzees manipulate simple tools: they use sticks to dig out insects, crumpled leaves to soak up water. Why, then, did they not also go on to use more complex tools? The answer is that an evolutionary change will only occur if it happens to fit in with an animal's general make-up: with its anatomy, its situation and its behaviour. All three depend very largely on where and how it gets its food. Being primarily fruit-eaters, chimpanzees were compelled to spend much of their time in the trees. They have, in consequence, retained feet and toes suitable for climbing, and so were unable to acquire the kind of foot which is suitable for bipedal movement on the ground. This, in turn, meant that they could not go on to develop the kind of complex tools which bipedal movement made possible.

Once they were able to move efficiently on the ground, man's ape-like ancestors were in a very different situation, similar in many ways to that of the present-day baboon. Like baboons, they must have eaten fruit and plants, eggs and game. No doubt they also dug for the long, tuberous roots which make up much of a baboon's diet in the dry season, and this offers one possible hint as to why the early hominids may first have taken to using tools. Digging up roots with finger-nails alone is both time-consuming and tedious, so much so that a dominant baboon will sometimes wait until an inferior has almost brought a root to the surface and then will walk calmly over and take the prize away. Such digging would be much easier if a baboon could use even a very simple tool, a stick perhaps or a pebble. Unluckily for baboons, they haven't learned to. Luckily for their future development, the hominids did.

Or perhaps the hominids first began to use tools not to dig for food, but as weapons to defend themselves against predators. In any case, by the time they reached the Australopithecine stage, the hominids had moved on to using sticks and pebbles to kill small animals for food. Instead of being preyed upon, they were the predators, and very much more efficient ones than any baboon or chimpanzee.

It would be hard to exaggerate the importance of predation—or hunting—in the development of man. Together with bipedalism and the use of tools, hunting was the principal element which set him on the evolutionary path that was to lead, ultimately, to his position of dominance over all other animals. Unfortunately, the early stages of man's career as a hunter are still shrouded in mystery. As we have seen, there are fossil remains to show that the small-brained Australopithecines used simple tools and that they hunted small animals. After that, however, the fossil remains are exceedingly scanty. Not until 500,000 years ago do we find plenty of evidence for the last stage before modern

BABOON HARVESTERS

Ancient Egyptian paintings show that baboons were once domesticated as pets, often seen on leashes in the market-place, sometimes doing tricks. In this 4,000-year-old tomb painting the pet baboons are depicted in a fig tree during harvest time. Although the animals seem to be eating the figs rather than dropping them in the baskets, it is thought they were really trained to aid the workers. Because they weighed less than grown men, the baboons had less chance of breaking the fragile branches of the fig trees as they gathered the fruit—work that was otherwise done by children or dwarfs.

man, a period of definitely human-like creatures with much larger brains. The remains of these early men have been found in Java and in Europe, in North Africa and in China near Peking. All of them had reached approximately the same stage of development, and we shall pick out one—Peking man—to serve as a representative of them all.

In a whole complex of ways, Peking man was a great improvement on the Australopithecines from whom he almost certainly descended. The Australopithecines could run and walk but not as efficiently as man. Peking man had a striding walk like ourselves, and that meant he could cover, without growing tired, the much longer distances needed to hunt large animals. He had learned to use fire. And instead of the simple chipped-pebble tools of Australopithecines, he had developed much more effective weapons: choppers and hand axes with which he was able to kill and cut open animals such as deer, rhino and even elephants.

Essentially, Peking man was much more efficient than *Australopithecus* because he possessed a larger and more complex brain. It was not, however, simply an across-the-board improved version of the Australopithecine brain. It was better only in a few, highly specific ways. Judged from our knowledge of the brain of modern man, the part that controlled the fingers and thumbs seems to have been much larger; so Peking man was better able to manufacture and to handle tools. And his brain appears to have been vastly better equipped to deal with abstractions: to memorize and to plan, to talk and to speculate.

We can see most clearly why the human brain developed in these two particular directions if we think of man primarily as a hunter—a hunter especially of large animals. To kill them, Peking man needed to make and to use more elaborate tools, which accounts for his improved control over his fingers and thumbs. He had to prepare his weapons for the hunt, which required foresight. To improve his weapons, he had to recall his past experiences, which required memory. And he had also to weigh what had happened in the past against possible situations that might arise in the future, which called for considerable powers of reflection. What is more, he had to co-operate closely with his fellow hunters. For while an individual Australopithecine could kill a small animal by himself, the hunting of large animals required co-operation, planning and mutual assistance.

As a hunter then, Peking man had to be able to communicate elaborate information to his fellows. But he also needed a means of communication for other purposes which grew out of his activities as a hunter, and these activities bring us to some of the most important social differences which came to distinguish man from all other primates. So far, throughout this book, we have stressed the similarities between humans on the one hand, and apes and monkeys on the other. It is time now to stress the contrasts, especially in their social relationships.

As we have seen, monkeys and some apes lead an extremely cohesive social existence. No advocate of togetherness could wish for anything more than that exhibited by, say, baboons or macaques. The members of a group are continually together. They move together, they eat together and they sleep together. No member of the group ever leaves the others for more than a few minutes at a time.

No doubt the first terrestrial animals from which man evolved were bound to each other almost as closely. It was the shift to hunting which transformed man's social behaviour and launched him along the route he was to follow for hundreds of thousands of years.

To begin with, hunting radically altered the relationship between the sexes by imposing on them a physical separation. For only the males could go off on the long treks required to hunt and kill large animals. The females were not able to accompany them because, for much of their adult lives, they were either pregnant or were nursing their infants. Going off at dawn and returning late in the evening, or perhaps even staying away for days at a time, the male hunters found themselves facing a problem that no monkey or ape ever had to contend with. They had to arrange some kind of meeting place where they could be sure to find their females and their infants. To achieve this purpose, the idea of the base camp was conceived. There the males of a group could meet up with the females when the hunt was over. There they could store their weapons between hunts. And there the infants would be comparatively safe while the males were away.

The invention of the base camp was one of the decisive steps in the history of man, as one can readily see by comparing his situation with that of any non-human primate, such as a baboon. A wounded or sick baboon must keep up with his group as it moves around in search of food. If he falls behind, he is almost certain to be killed by predators. But once men had conceived the idea of the base camp, the individual members of the group were very much less vulnerable, for they had only to reach the camp to be safe. There, a man could rest and recover his strength or treat his injuries. A minor virus disease or a badly sprained ankle would no longer be fatal, as it must be—all too often— to a baboon. It would be merely an inconvenience. Thus men's chances of survival were vastly increased.

And so was the sense of mutual dependence that bound the members of a group together. A sick man who was helped to the camp and allowed to rest there, fed by the others while he recovered his strength, would naturally be grateful to his companions. Were the situation to be reversed, he would do the same for them—and no doubt he often did.

So gradually a growing sense of mutual trust was built up, and it was not confined only to the comparatively rare occasions when within the membership of a group someone of the group happened to find himself in danger. As a result of hunting, men and women came to rely on each other—as no monkeys or apes do—for food. Returning from the hunt, the males would bring back meat which the females were eager to share. In exchange for it, the males were given their share of the plants and roots the females had gathered, and this daily sharing of food must have further strengthened the bonds which held the members of a group together.

By the time they reached this stage, men and women had a great deal to communicate to each other. Planning base camps, sharing food, reassuring injured companions—all these activities required a system of communication that went far beyond simple expressions of alarm or threat or fear. We know how man met this need. He retained the system of communication by gestures or facial expressions used by monkeys and apes; and, in addition, he also acquired a far more elaborate language based on sounds, which enabled him to communicate ideas.

He developed, in other words, a system of quite arbitrary symbols which,

ATTENTION

EXCITEMENT

by common agreement, came to represent certain facts, or situations, or thoughts. Of all the advances made by man, the invention of a spoken language probably did the most to set him apart from every other kind of animal. Pause a moment while you read, and try to imagine what your life would be like without words. Try, for example, to remember what happened the last time you saw a friend, or try to plan what you will do tomorrow, simply in terms of visual images without using words at all. You will not get very far. For we do not use words merely to express ideas or plans or recapture memories. We actually think in words and, without them, the great mass of human thought processes simply could not exist.

Yet, although language has played so vital a role in the emergence of man, the actual processes by which it came into being remain a total mystery. All one can say with certainty is that language must have been created in very gradual stages as men slowly enlarged their intellectual powers, and that it, too, developed as part of the feedback process.

FEAR

Bɪᴘᴇᴅᴀʟɪsᴍ, tools, hunting, language—put them all together, and the feedback process turns out to have been one of extraordinary complexity. And so was the brain that emerged from it. As our ancestors progressed, from *Australopithecus* to Peking man, and from Peking man to *Homo sapiens*, their brains grew steadily larger. The brain cells themselves became more elaborate, and so did the marvellously intricate passage-ways that connected them. These improvements in the human brain occurred as a response to the demands made on it. Alternatively, of course, one can look at the same phenomenon from the opposite point of view and say that, as the human brain improved, men and women became both more knowledgeable and more competent. The process worked both ways, and the result was that man was able to acquire an increasingly elaborate culture.

ANGER

At one point, a more effective hunting technique would be added to the pool of knowledge; at another, a new kind of tool; at a third, some useful refinement in language. With every additional contribution, there was a greater mass of knowledge to be passed on, and that knowledge had to be learned by each new generation of children as part of the process of growing up.

Obviously, this need made great demands on the children. In order to learn how to talk and to think, to plan and to make complicated tools, children, too, had to possess bigger brains. What is more, as the body of human knowledge grew, children needed additional time in which to absorb all the traditional information that was passed down to them. It was these twin needs that together were responsible for perhaps the most extraordinary of all the changes which have marked man's evolutionary history. A little reflection will show that, as the human brain grew larger, human females were faced with a peculiarly difficult situation. An infant's skull had to be large enough to house the enlarged human brain. At the same time, it also had to be small enough to emerge through the mother's birth canal. The obvious solution, one might suppose, would have been for females to acquire a larger birth canal. But they couldn't. For the characteristics needed for bipedal walking made the enlargement of the birth canal a physical impossibility beyond a certain limit.

JOY

So, instead of the adaptations taking place in the mothers, they took place in the infants. Gradually, over a period of perhaps several hundreds of thousands of years, human infants came to be born at a far less advanced stage of development than infant monkeys or apes. One can, in fact, almost say that they came

SADNESS

to be born like premature babies who would acquire after birth the characteristics they had not been able to develop inside the womb.

It is impossible not to be astonished by the marvellously intricate pattern of complexities that combined to produce this shift. How, after all, could human infants be born at a less advanced stage and still survive? Put very simply, the answer is that, unlike monkeys or apes, human infants did not have to cling to their mothers' hair as soon as they were born. They had mothers who walked upright; who, living in base camps, did not need to be continually on the move; mothers, in short, who were both able and willing to hold and carry them. Given such mothers, human infants did not need the sophisticated control over their nervous system that is typical of the new-born monkey or ape. They could be helpless for a very long time and still survive.

Their situation, in fact, was rather like that of an airline traveller. Able to carry only so much luggage, he has to balance the advantages of one item against another. A human infant could only emerge through his mother's birth canal if his brain were small. So out went the highly developed nervous system of the new-born monkey or ape; and in its place came the additional brain cells needed to handle the unique refinements of human culture.

A human baby, of course, is not born with a brain that can enable him to speak fluently or to solve mathematical equations. What he does have is a brain with the potential to grow to the required size. Today, he is born with a brain only one-quarter the size it will eventually reach. In the time of Peking man, the human brain did not expand so much after birth. None the less, Peking man's infants must have been quite helpless for several months after they were born. They must have remained dependent on their mothers for several years, and during this period they had time to master the complicated culture that was handed down to them.

VIKI, THE TALKING CHIMP

Although chimpanzees have the necessary equipment of jaw, tongue and larynx, their brains do not permit them to say more than a few simple words. The drawings show how a pet chimpanzee named Viki was taught to say "mama". First her lips were manipulated to form an "m" to supplement the "ah" sound she made naturally. Two weeks later all she needed to say "mama" was a touch of a finger (second drawing). A little later she still preferred a gentle prod to help her to say the word, and would lean towards her owner's hand (third drawing). Soon she could say "mama" on her own; she used it so indiscriminately that she clearly had no idea of its meaning.

M EANWHILE, yet another very important change was taking place in the human animal. Physically, as well as socially, the sexual relationship between men and women was transformed, and this transformation was in a direction that set human beings apart from all non-human primates. Among monkeys, as we have seen, copulation is exceedingly periodic. The females are receptive for only a few days in every month. They conceive their young during only a few months of the year, and they do not engage in sexual activity for several months after they have borne an infant.

Human females behave quite differently; they are, potentially, sexually receptive at almost any time. They can copulate throughout most of their monthly cycle and also at all times of the year. Why did the shift take place? What advantage did it produce? These are intriguing questions, and unfortunately we can only speculate on the answers.

Possibly human females became able to copulate at practically any time in order to meet the problem posed by their infants' long period of dependence. For suppose that, like monkey females, human mothers had remained unable to have sexual intercourse as long as their infants were still dependent. They would have been cut off from sexual activity for years at a time, and the bonds which united the females and the males of a group would inevitably have been weakened—perhaps seriously. But if, as actually happened, a mother could start having sex again soon after her baby was born, this danger would have been neatly avoided.

Or perhaps the shift was an adaptation acquired to meet a new psychological situation that developed when men became hunters. While sex is a pleasurable activity, it can also be a very disruptive influence among aggressive animals that live together in groups. It is true that apes and monkeys seem well able to handle the problem as long as they are in their natural habitat. But hunting must have made human males more aggressive, and sexual competition may well have come to agitate them, as it certainly agitates us—their descendants. To hunters, in particular, any fights over sex would have been exceedingly damaging, since fighting and ill will would have impaired both their ability and their desire to co-operate while out hunting. If, however, their females were permanently receptive, the men would not have been so likely to fight over this issue. For one receptive female could have satisfied the sexual needs of any one man at almost any time. And if every adult male in the group had a female to himself, the possibility of disruptive fights over sex would have been greatly reduced.

IF this theory is correct, we owe the institution of family life to the fact that our ancestors were once hunters. Still, such a reconstruction of the past is only speculation: we do not know for certain that hunting was really the main element behind the change in human sexual behaviour. But when we turn to the relationships between different groups, hunting does stand out as the most likely cause of yet another revolutionary shift which, once again, helped to set men and women apart from all non-human primates.

Because of language, groups of humans intermingle far more than the non-human primates. The males and the females intermarry, and we can trace this difference back to the time when men ceased to be predominantly vegetarians and became hunters instead. Consider what was involved. As plants and roots and fruit tend to be fairly evenly distributed in any one area, one group of vegetarians has little reason to risk danger by invading another group's range. The supply of game, in contrast, is much more restricted, and hunting man must frequently have been tempted to invade his neighbour's land. Then what would have happened? Obviously the invaded groups would have resisted because, if they had been allowed to trespass, the invaders would have either killed or disturbed the game that the home group wanted for itself.

One can reasonably assume that it was this kind of invasion and resistance, repeated over and over again, that transformed men into animals with a possessive sense of territory: every group must have come to feel that its territory belonged to it alone and was worth fighting for. From such crude beginnings there was eventually to spring the concept of a communal land which the inhabitants were prepared to defend, if necessary, at the cost of their lives. The city-state, the kingdom, the nation—all had their roots in the hunters' need to protect their game against outsiders.

Territorial defence—or offence—has always been the prime cause of war; yet, paradoxically, it was also the foundation of social intercourse between different peoples. For war, after all, is a very expensive business. Today it can kill millions, and even when men were merely simple hunters possessed of no weapons more lethal than a hand axe, fighting between groups must have cost them dearly. It not only endangered their lives. It also disturbed the game and dissipated the energies that could have been spent far more profitably in killing animals. So, in the interests of survival, neighbouring bands of hunters gradually learned to keep the peace, and the principal instrument they employed was exogamy—marriage outside the group.

To account for the emergence of exogamy in this way is perhaps to over-state the element of deliberation involved, or so some anthropologists maintain. The system of exogamy was probably not instituted consciously as a way to establish alliances. Still, it certainly did become a regular part of human behaviour, and it did provide, in practice, a basis for alliances between different groups. Brothers and sisters, cousins and nieces and nephews, all bound by close emotional ties, were spread by the practice of exogamy throughout neighbouring bands. There they served at once as hostages and as diplomats, making members of different groups better acquainted and so reducing the chances of mutually destructive conflict.

THE practice of exogamy also had two other consequences of enormous importance to the evolution of man. As the members of different groups came to know each other, they were able to pool their knowledge and to exchange ideas: on hunting techniques, on ways to make tools, on language. This was yet another of the steps which took men far beyond the most advanced of non-human primates. Although groups of monkeys and apes can pass down knowledge from one generation to the next, their knowledge is inevitably confined to what the members of each group have learned. But once the members of human groups began to marry outsiders, and thus to spread beyond their own relatively narrow limits, the knowledge of one group became potentially the knowledge of all, and the possibility of human progress was vastly increased.

This was a cultural advance; it was improvement and progress through rational exchange. But biologically also, exogamy must have given a tremendous boost to the course of human evolution. Consider what happens if you try to make combinations out of three letters: A, B and C. The number of possible combinations is extremely limited. Add another letter and the number of possible combinations is enormously increased and it continues to grow, in rapidly multiplying progression, as more letters are added. A very similar progression must have occurred with the number of genetic combinations that dictate the physical make-up of humans. So long as each group remained an isolated unit, the number of possible combinations was relatively meagre. But when members of different groups inter-married, the gene pool was enlarged by a vastly greater number of combinations, and so the chances of favourable biological changes occurring were enormously improved.

Although we cannot yet be sure, it seems likely that these advances—biological and cultural, social and sexual—had all begun to exert their influence on human evolution by about half a million years ago. They set the way for all the later evolutionary advances which man was to enjoy, notably in the size of his brain and the complexity of his thinking, until finally he became what he is to-day—master of the planet. As a rational, self-conscious animal, he stands far beyond any other primate. But reason, after all, is only one part of that fantastically complicated organism which constitutes man. Anatomically, he is not so very different from the great apes. In some of his social relationships, his behaviour curiously resembles that of baboons and macaques. Emotionally, before he grows up and learns to behave as society dictates, he is not so far removed from the chimpanzee. Certainly man deserves to be placed in a family of his own; he has come a long way since his ape-like ancestors descended from the trees. But not, perhaps, as far as we should like to think as we look with a mixture of curiosity, awe and a strange sense of uneasiness at the monkeys and the apes who stare back at us—their relatives—from their perches in the forest.

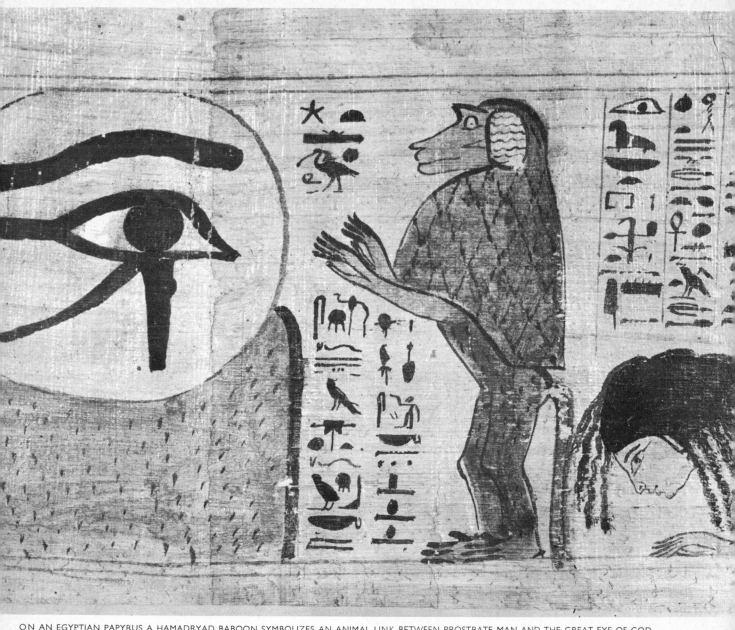

ON AN EGYPTIAN PAPYRUS A HAMADRYAD BABOON SYMBOLIZES AN ANIMAL LINK BETWEEN PROSTRATE MAN AND THE GREAT EYE OF GOD.

Monkeys in Man's World

East and West, wild or captive, wherever monkeys and apes are seen, physical kinship with man has long been recognized. But only in recent years have scientists begun to gather evidence bearing on social and psychological bonds which link these primates with man. Though we still have much to learn, the results, as this book testifies, have already been extraordinarily rewarding.

MACAQUES SWARM unmolested over a street in Ajodhya, in northern India, holy capital of legendary King Rama. To protect against simian theft, merchants use bamboo screens.

ON A TEMPLE STATUE in Banaras a bonnet macaque sits with the aplomb of a pigeon in Trafalgar Square. Like the sacred langurs, macaques are fed and pampered throughout India.

In the East, a Sacred Nuisance

Any study of man's long relationship with the simians must include the East, where apes and monkeys have always lived cheek by jowl with people, becoming a part of their very culture. Effigies of Hanuman, the monkey god, who presides over the arts of magic and healing, hang in most Hindu homes. Out of doors, live monkeys wander the streets, protected by the Hindu belief that all living things carry a spark of divinity, and therefore must not be killed. Particularly in northern India, where the pull of religion is strong, these intelligent animals romp through the cities and villages as though they owned them. Occasionally they are rounded up and deported to the jungle, but every day new accounts of monkey mischief appear in the papers. Items: raiding a train and squirting tooth-paste on sleeping passengers; stealing 10,000 rupees from a bank clerk; and invading a hospital, grabbing a baby from its mother and dropping it out of a window.

THE HINDU MONKEY DANCE, performed in Bali, honours the monkey god, Hanuman. According to Hindu legend, Hanuman and his monkey army helped Prince Rama to recover his beautiful bride Sita, who had been abducted by a giant. In this Balinese interpretation, the women in the centre represent Sita, while the ring of seated men mimics the monkey army.

A RHESUS MACAQUE and tourists eye one another in a Florida commercial wild-life reservation. There animals are displayed in a setting which closely resembles their natural habitat.

In the West, Foster-Homes

The wide-eyed little orang-outang on the right, born behind bars and nurtured in an incubator, typifies the traditional situation of monkeys and apes in the West, where they are confined primarily to circuses, zoos and laboratories. However, it was Japan which, by establishing a primate research centre in 1948, first formally recognized the importance of primatology as a science. Today, Western scientists, besides manning their own primate research centres, are conducting intensive field studies as well. And perhaps the most important development in primatology is the growing awareness that only a combination of laboratory study and observations made in the field will produce the fully rounded picture man desires of his closest cousins—for a better understanding both of them and of himself.

PAMPERED LIKE AN HEIR APPARENT BY ST. LOUIS ZOO KEEPERS, AN INFANT

ANG-OUTANG PEERS THROUGH THE GLASS OF AN INCUBATOR. ITS MOTHER, GROWN LISTLESS IN CAPTIVITY, HAD DECLINED TO TAKE CARE OF IT.

Bibliography

General

Boulenger, E. G., *Apes and Monkeys*. Harrap, 1936.

Buettner-Janusch, John, ed., *Evolutionary and Genetic Biology of the Primates* (vol. 1, 1963, vol. 2, 1964). Academic Press.

†Buettner-Janusch, J., and others, *The Relatives of Man*. Annals of the New York Academy of Sciences (vol. 102, art. 2), December 1962.

*Clark, W. E. LeGros, *The Antecedents of Man*. Quadrangle, 1960. *History of the Primates* (4th ed.). University of Chicago Press, 1963.

Cockrum, E. Lendell, *Introduction to Mammalogy*. Ronald Press, New York, 1962.

†Elliot, Daniel Giraud, *A Review of the Primates* (3 vols.). Monographs of the American Museum of Natural History, 1913.

Hill, W. C. Osman, *Primates: Comparative Anatomy and Taxonomy* (vols. 1–5: 1953, 1955, 1957, 1960, 1962). Wiley.

†Hofner, H., A. H. Schultz, and D. Stark, eds., *Primatologia* (vol. 1, 1956). S. Karger: Phiebig, New York.

Hooton, Earnest Albert, *Man's Poor Relations*. Doubleday, 1942. *Up from the Ape* (rev. ed.). Collier-Macmillan, 1946.

Howells, William White, *Mankind in the Making*. Doubleday, 1959.

Napier, John and N. A. Barnicot, eds., *The Primates*. Symposia of the Zoological Society of London (No. 10), 1963.

*Sanderson, Ivan T., *The Monkey Kingdom*. Chiltern, Pa., 1963.

Classification and Evolution

Coon, Carleton S., *The Origin of Races*. Knopf, 1962. *The Story of Man* (2nd ed.). Knopf, 1962.

Howell, F. Clark, and François Bourlière, eds., *African Ecology and Human Evolution*. Aldine, Chicago, Ill., 1963.

Moore, Ruth, *Man, Time and Fossils* (rev. ed.). Knopf, 1961.

Romer, Alfred S., *Vertebrate Paleontology* (2nd ed.). University of Chicago Press, 1945.

†Simons, Elwyn L., "The Early Relatives of Man". *Scientific American* (vol. 211, no. 1), July 1964.

Simpson, George Gaylord, *The Meaning of Evolution*. Yale University Press, 1949, 1960. †*The Principles of Classification and a Classification of Mammals*. Bulletin of the American Museum of Natural History (vol. 85), 1945.

Tax, Sol, ed., *Horizons of Anthropology*. Aldine, Chicago, Ill., 1964.

Washburn, Sherwood L., ed., *Classification and Human Evolution*. Aldine, Chicago, Ill., 1963. *Social Life of Early Man*. Aldine, Chicago, Ill., 1961.

Regional Books

Attenborough, David, *Bridge to the Past*. Harper & Row, 1962.

Gee, E. P., *The Wild Life of India*. Collins, 1964.

Lima, Eladio da Cruz, *Mammals of Amazonia* (vol. 1). Museo Paranese Emilio Goeldi de Historia Natural e Ethnografia, 1945.

Moorehead, Alan, *No Room in the Ark*. Harper & Row, 1959.

Specific Primates

†Goodall, Jane, "My Life Among Wild Chimpanzees". *National Geographic* (vol. 124, no. 2), August 1963.

Gregory, William King, ed., *The Anatomy of the Gorilla*. Columbia University Press, 1950.

Harrisson, Barbara, *Orang-utan*. Doubleday, 1963.

Hayes, Cathy, *The Ape In Our House*. Harper & Row, 1951.

†Kortlandt, Adriaan, "Chimpanzees in the Wild". *Scientific American* (vol. 206, no. 5), May 1962.

Schaller, George B., *The Mountain Gorilla*. University of Chicago Press, 1963. *The Year of the Gorilla*. University of Chicago Press, 1964.

†Washburn, S. L., and Irven DeVore, "The Social Life of Baboons". *Scientific American* (vol. 204, no. 6), June 1961.

Yerkes, Robert M., *Chimpanzees*. Yale University Press, 1943.

Yerkes, Robert M. and Ada W., *The Great Apes*. Yale University Press, 1929.

General Behaviour

Bliss, Eugene L., *Roots of Behavior*. Harper & Row, 1962.

†Broadhurst, P. L., *The Science of Animal Behaviour*. Penguin, 1963.

Carpenter, C. R., *Naturalistic Behavior of Nonhuman Primates*. Pennsylvania State University Press, 1964.

DeVore, Irven, ed., *Primate Behavior*. Holt, Rinehart and Winston, New York, 1965.

Etkin, William, ed., *Social Behavior and Organization Among Vertebrates*. University of Chicago Press, 1964.

*Klüver, Heinrich, *Behavior Mechanisms in Monkeys*. University of Chicago Press, 1933.

Roe, Anne, and George Gaylord Simpson, eds., *Behavior and Evolution*. Yale University Press, 1958.

†Sahlins, Marshall D., "The Origin of Society". *Scientific American* (vol. 203, no. 3), September 1960.

*Scott, John Paul, *Animal Behavior*. University of Chicago Press, 1958.

†Southwick, Charles H., ed., *Primate Social Behavior*. Van Nostrand, 1963.

Zuckerman, S., *The Social Life of Monkeys and Apes*. Harcourt, Brace, New York, 1932.

Mother-Infant Behaviour

Foss, B. M., ed., *Determinants of Infant Behaviour* (vol. 1, 1961, vol. 2, 1963). Wiley.

†Harlow, Harry F., "Love in Infant Monkeys." *Scientific American* (vol. 200, no. 6), June 1959. "Of Love in Infants." *Natural History* (vol. 69, no. 5), May 1960.

†Harlow, Harry F. and Margaret K., "A Study of Animal Affection". *Natural History* (vol. 70, no. 10), December 1961. "Social Deprivation in Monkeys." *Scientific American* (vol. 207, no. 5), November 1962.

Kellogg, W. N. and L. A., *The Ape and the Child*. McGraw-Hill, 1933.

Mitchell, P. Chalmers, *The Childhood of Animals*. Heinemann, 1912.

Rheingold, Harriet L., ed., *Maternal Behavior in Mammals*. Wiley, 1963.

Miscellaneous

Darwin, Charles, *Expression of the Emotions in Man and Animals*. Philosophical Library, New York, 1955.

*Hanrahan, James Stephen, and David Bushnell, *Space Biology*. Basic Books, New York, 1960.

Janson, H. W., *Apes and Ape Lore in the Middle Ages and the Renaissance*. University of London Press, 1952.

Knapp, Peter H., ed., *Expression of the Emotions in Man*. International Universities Press, 1963.

McDermott, William, *The Ape In Antiquity*. Johns Hopkins University Studies in Archaeology (no. 27), 1938.

Morris, Desmond, *The Biology of Art*. Knopf, 1962.

Polyak, Stephen, *The Vertebrate Visual System*. University of Chicago Press, 1958.

Films

Carpenter, C. R., *Howler Monkeys of Barro Colorado Island*. Pennsylvania State University, 1960. 27 minutes, sound, black and white.

DeVore, I., and S. L. Washburn: *Baboon Behavior*, 1961, 31 minutes, sound, colour; *Baboon Ecology*, 1963, 21 minutes, sound, colour; *Baboon Social Organization*, 1963, 17 minutes, sound, colour; University of California.

Harlow, H. F., *Mother Love*. Carousel Films: Columbia Broadcasting System, 1960, 26 minutes, sound, black and white.

Schaller, George, *Mountain Gorilla*. New York Zoological Society, 1960, 16 minutes, sound, colour.

Southwick, C. H., *The Rhesus Monkey in India*. Johns Hopkins University, 1962, 22 minutes, sound, colour.

All films listed are available for rental at the Psychological Cinema Register, Pennsylvania State University, Pa., U.S.A.

*Also available in paperback.
†Only available in paperback.

Credits

The sources for the illustrations in this book are shown below.
Credits for pictures from left to right are separated by commas, top to bottom by dashes.

Cover—Larry Burrows
8—Jorg Klages
10, 11—Enid Kotschnig
12—drawings by Rudolf Freund
13—drawings by Margaret Estey reprinted with permission from Dr. John Buettner-Janusch from *Introduction to Physical Anthropology* © 1965 John Wiley & Sons Inc.
14—top drawing Rudolf Freund and Margaret Estey, bottom drawings by Margaret Estey
15—drawing by Margaret Estey
17—Nina Leen
18, 19—drawing left and background by George V. Kelvin; figures by Joseph Cellini
20 to 23—Larry Burrows
24, 25—Loomis Dean, Terence Spencer
26—Loomis Dean
27—David Attenborough
28, 29—W. Suschitzky
30—A. W. Ambler from Photo Researchers
31—H. Sprankel except bottom New York Zoological Society
32—Jean-Jacques Petter
33—Paul Popper Ltd.
34—Ylla from Rapho-Guillumette
36—drawings by Rudolf Freund; diagrams by Mark Binn
38—drawing by Rudolf Freund and Margaret Estey
39—drawing by Margaret Estey—drawing by Rudolf Freund and Margaret Estey
43—Nina Leen
44, 45—map by Matt Greene; symbols by Otto van Eersel
46—Nina Leen
47—Shelly Grossman—R. Van Nostrand from Photo Researchers, Nina Leen
48, 49—Douglas Faulkner, Nina Leen—Shelly Grossman
50—Nina Leen
51—Don Uhrbrock
52, 53—J. & L. Kern, Larry Burrows

54—E. S. Ross, E. P. Gee
55—Okapai Tierbilder
56—Eric Kirkland
57—Eric Kirkland except bottom Jorg Klages
58, 59—Jorg Klages
60—Ralph Morse courtesy of Animal Talent Scouts Inc. and L. D'Essen & V. Phifer
62—drawings by Otto van Eersel
63 to 67—drawings by Enid Kotschnig
65—quote from *No Room in the Ark* by Alan Moorehead reprinted with the permission of Harper and Row and Hamish Hamilton Ltd. publishers
71—A. Kortlandt
72, 73—Ralph Morse courtesy of Animal Talent Scouts Inc. and L. D'Essen & V. Phifer
74, 75—Nina Leen
76, 77—Terence Spencer, Paul Popper Ltd.
78—Terence Spencer
79—New York Zoological Society
80—Michael Rougier
81—courtesy The American Museum of Natural History
82, 83—drawings by Jack J. Kunz
84—Phyllis Jay University of California Berkeley
86—drawing by Enid Kotschnig
89—drawings by Rudolf Freund
90, 91—The University of Chicago Press
93—adapted by Enid Kotschnig from Phyllis Jay "The Common Langur of North India" in *Primate Behavior : Field Studies of Monkeys and Apes* edited by Irven DeVore. New York: Holt, Rinehart and Winston, Inc. 1965
95—Alfred Eisenstaedt
96, 97—George Holton from Photo Researchers, Suzanne Ripley University of California Berkeley
98, 99—Suzanne Ripley Univer-

sity of California Berkeley except top right Phyllis Jay University of California Berkeley
100—Phyllis Jay University of California Berkeley
101—Alfred Eisenstaedt
102, 103—Phyllis Jay University of California Berkeley—Suzanne Ripley University of California Berkeley
104, 105—Irven DeVore
108—drawings by Rudolf Freund, bar graph by Matt Greene
110, 111—drawings by Otto van Eersel
115, 116—Irven DeVore
117—Stanley Washburn
118—Irven DeVore—Stanley Washburn
119—Stanley Washburn
120—Irven DeVore
121—Stanley Washburn except top left Irven DeVore
122, 123—Irven DeVore
124, 125—Irven DeVore except top right Stanley Washburn
126, 127—Stanley Washburn
128—Terence Spencer
130—Otto van Eersel
131—Otto van Eersel based on drawings in paper by J. R. Napier, Unit of Primatology and Human Evolution, Royal Free Hospital School of Medicine London
132—from Phyllis Jay "The Common Langur of North India" in *Primate Behavior : Field Studies of Monkeys and Apes* edited by Irven DeVore. New York: Holt, Rinehart and Winston, Inc. 1965
134, 135—drawings by Rudolf Freund and Margaret Estey
137—Terence Spencer
138, 139—drawings by Leo and Diane Dillon
140, 141—Irven DeVore, Stanley Washburn
142, 143—Irven DeVore
144, 145—Sherwood L. Washburn University of California

Berkeley except top left J. Wightman
146, 147—A. Kortlandt
148, 149—Sherwood L. Washburn University of California Berkeley
150—Novosti Press Agency Moscow USSR
152—from *Historia Naturalis* by Ulysses Aldrovandus 1642
153—drawings by Enid Kotschnig
157—drawings by Enid Kotschnig
159—Yale Joel
160 to 163—Yale Joel courtesy the Oregon Regional Primate Research Center
164, 165—Yale Joel courtesy Yerkes Regional Primate Research Center of Emory University
166, 167—Fred Sponholz University of Wisconsin
168—Phyllis Jay University of California Berkeley—Stanley Washburn—Suzanne Ripley University of California Berkeley, Irven DeVore
169—Larry Burrows
170, 171—Alan Clifton courtesy Desmond Morris except top right Jack Garofalo from *Paris-Match*
172—Wide World
173, 174, 175—Fritz Goro
176—Elisabeth Elliot from Magnum Photos
178—drawing by Enid Kotschnig
180—drawing by Enid Kotschnig
182, 183—drawings by Rudolf Freund and Margaret Estey
184—drawings by Enid Kotschnig
187—from *l'Homme et l'Animal* published by Editions Robert Laffont courtesy the British Museum
188—James Burke—Alfred Eisenstaedt
189—Van Bucher from Photo Researchers
190, 191—Leonard McCombe, Nina Leen
Back Cover—Otto van Eersel

Acknowledgments

The editors of this book are particularly indebted to S. L. Washburn, Professor of Anthropology, University of California, Berkeley, who read the book in its entirety. They also want to thank Phyllis Jay, Jane Lancaster and Suzanne Ripley, Department of Anthropology, University of California, Berkeley, and G. E. Erikson, Assistant Professor of Anatomy, Harvard Medical School. Others who helped in their special fields are R. J. Andrew, Department of Zoology, Yale University; Bernard V. Bothmer, Curator of Ancient Art, Brooklyn Museum; François Bourlière, Professor, Faculté de Médecine de Paris; John Buettner-Janusch, Associate Professor of Anthropology, Yale University; C. R. Carpenter, Professor of Psychology, Pennsylvania State University; Bruce Coleman; Joseph A. Davis Jr., Curator of Mammals, New York Zoological Park; K.R.L. Hall, Professor of Psychology, University of Bristol; Harry F. Harlow, Director, Primate Laboratory, University of Wisconsin; Richard Howard, Director, Arnold Arboretum, Harvard University; Caroline Jarvis, London Zoological Society; Malcolm C. McKenna, Assistant Curator, Department of Vertebrate Paleontology, The American Museum of Natural History;

Desmond Morris, Curator of Mammals, London Zoological Society; John Napier, Royal Free Hospital, Medical School, London; David Pilbeam, Department of Geology, Yale University; Edward S. Ross, Department of Entomology, California Academy of Sciences, San Francisco; Paul E. Simonds, Department of Anthropology, University of Oregon; Elwyn L. Simons, Associate Professor of Geology, Curator of Vertebrate Paleontology, Peabody Museum, Yale University; Nigel Sitwell; R. A. Stirton, Professor of Paleontology, Curator of Mammals and Director of the Museum of Paleontology, University of California, Berkeley; Richard G. Van Gelder, Chairman and Associate Curator, Department of Mammalogy, The American Museum of Natural History and Maurice Wilson. The editors also want to thank William Montagna, Director, Flo Louise Fields, Marjorie LaSalle, C. W. de Lannoy Jr., R. M. Malinow, John G. Roth and William C. Young of the Oregon Regional Primate Research Center, Beaverton; Geoffrey H. Bourne, Director, Irwin S. Bernstein, Frances L. Fitz-Gerald, Charles M. Rogers and Murray E. Townsend of the Yerkes Regional Primate Research Center of Emory University, Atlanta.

Index

Numerals in italics indicate a photograph or painting of the subject mentioned.

Adaptations: behavioural v. biological, 64; in birth patterns, 183-184; in body structure, 39, 64, 82, 179, 183; in brain structure, 10, 13, 183; for canine teeth, 38; to captivity, 40-42, 51, 68, 70, 77, 109, 110, 133, 156, 190, 191; of digestive systems, 37, 54, 152; of finger- and toe-nails, 10; for grasping, 10-11, 13-14; to ground living, 38, 135, 152, 179; in group behaviour, 185; learned, 89; for locomotion, 62, 63, 64, 65, 82; by man, 42; to man's residential areas, 136, 188; against predators, 115, 152-153, 180-181; for protection, 37-38, 41, 94, 179; to seasons, 54; in sex differences, 38; in sex instincts, 184-185; by skin pads, 38-39; social, 107, 113; for survival, 131; in temperament, 41; to temperatures, 12; to tree living, 10, 12, 16, 94; in use of sense organs, 10, 12

Africa: angwantibos of, 28-29; apes of, 15, 62, 63, 65, 67, 177; baboons of, map 44-45, 107, 113, 114, 115, 144, 145, 152, 168; colobus monkeys of, 54; early man of, 177-178; fossils in, map 44-45, 178, 179, 181; galagos of, 28; gorillas of, 63, 136; monkeys of, 35, 36-37, 56-57; pottos of, 12-13, 28-29, 30, 31; prosimians of, 11; vervets of, 152

African bushman, territorial ranges of, chart 130

Albert National Park, 63

Alcoholism, experiment on chimpanzees, 164-165

Amboseli Reserve Park, Kenya, 104-105, 144-145

Angwantibos, 28-29

Antelopes, 145

Anthropoid apes, map 44-45, 71

Anthropology: human behaviour determinants, 151-158, 178; relationship to primatology, 9

Apes, 61-71; of Africa, 62, 63, 65, 67, 177; arboreal, 61, 62, 72-73, 96-97, 130; of Asia, 15, 62; artistic ability of, 170, 171; daily schedules of, 129-130; disposition of, 161; eating habits of, 16; genealogy of, chart 18-19; genera of, 15; group behaviour of, 129-130, 131-133; growth patterns of, chart 86; habitat of, map 44-45, 177; maturation of, chart 86; sense organs of, 13; similarity to man, 16, 178, 186; social groups of, 129-130; traditions of, 130-131. See also Chimpanzees; Gibbons; Gorillas; Orang-outangs

Arabia, baboons of, 113

Arboreal apes, 61, 62, 72-73, 96-97, 130

Arboreal monkeys, 36, 38, chart 130; diagram 131

Archaeological research, 178-179

Arm positions, of gibbon and macaque, 62

Art: of chimpanzees, 155-156, 170, 171; of gorillas, 155; of orang-outangs, 155

Asia: apes of, 15, 62; langurs of, 54; lorises of, 12, 28, 29; monkeys of, 36-37; prosimians of, 11; tarsiers of, 22-23; tree shrews of, 10-11

Auca Indians, and monkeys, 176, 177

Australopithecines (ape men), 178-181

Australopithecus, fossils of, 178

Avahi (lemur), chart 18-19

Aye-aye (lemur), chart 18-19, 32, 33

Baboons, 89, 94, 107-114, 126-127, 128; adaptations to ground living, 152; of Africa, map 44-45, 107, 113, 114, 115, 144, 145, 152, 168; of Arabia, 113; body structure of, 37, 134; canine teeth of, 116, 117, 134; communication of, 116, 118, 119, 134; death reactions of, 134-135; discipline among, 108-109, 124-125; eating habits of, 113, 133, 140-141, 142-145, 152, 154-155, 180, 181; of Egypt, 58, 59, 180, 187; of Ethiopia, 58, 113; fear of the unknown among, 131; field studies of, 89, 111, 115, 131, 133-134, 141, 154, 168-169; geladas, 58; genealogy of, chart 18-19; grooming of, 107, 115, 122; group behaviour of, 40-41, 104-105, 111, 113, 115, 118, 119, 124, 125, 133-135, 137, diagram 138-139, 140-141, 146-147, 154, 180-182; habitat of, map 44-45, 58, 113; growth patterns of, 89, 119; habitat of, map 44-45, 58, 113; Hamadryad, 40-42, 58-59, 110, 113, 187; illness of, 182; infants of, 89, 94, 120-125, 134, 146; of Kenya, 104-105, 114; leadership among, 94, 111, 116, 118, 119, 146; learning ability of, 89, 134, 141, 180; locomotion of, 37, 121; mating habits of, 113; mother-child relationships, 89, 110-111, 120-121; as pets, 180; physical characteristics of, 38, 40, 58, 89, 116, 117, 134; as predators, 142, 143; predators of, 38, 139, 146, 148-149; protective tactics of, 37, 116, 121, 131, 134, 135, 140-141, 146-149, 152-153, 182; reactions to strangers, 131-133; sex differences of, 38, 94, 134; sex hostility of, 40; skin pads of, 128, 129; sleeping habits of, 113, 128, 129, 135, 181; social groups of, 40, 42, 94, 110, 111, 113, 121-123, 144, 145, 181-182; status among, 42, 107, 111, 118, 119, 124; temperament of, 40, 41, 107, 108, 111, 112, 113, 123; territorial limits of, chart 130, 131, 137, 144, 145; and use of weapons, 152-153; vision of, 140-141

Barro Colorado Island, monkeys of, 39-40

Base camps, 182-184

Behavioural testing, of orang-outangs, 164, 165

Biochemical studies, 7

Birth patterns: adaptations in, 183-184; of man, 184; of monkeys, 31, 85, 90; of mouse lemurs, 24

Body structure; adaptations in, 39, 64, 82, 179, 183; of *Australopithecus*, 178; of baboons, 37, 134; changes by exogamy, 186; of chimpanzees 11, 15, 182-183; of colobus monkeys, 37; differences between apes and monkeys, 62; evolution of, 16; experiments with, 162; of gibbons, 15, 62, 63, 64, 135; of gorillas, 65, 82-83, 90; of indriidae, 152; of langurs, 37; of lorises, 10; macaques, 11, 62, 82-83; of man, 14, 64, 65, 82-83, 178, 183; of marmosets, 11; of orang-outangs, 15, 63; of Peking man, 181; of primates, 15, 82-83; of spider monkey, 39; of tarsiers, 10, 14, 15, 23; of tree shrews, 10

Bonnet macaques, 188

Borneo: langurs of, 53; monkeys of, 168, 169; orang-outangs of, 63; tree shrews of, 20

Brain, of lemur, 13; of macaque, 13; of monkeys, 14; of tree shrew, 13

Brain activity, experiments in, 159

Brain structure, adaptations in, 10, 13, 183

"Brassau, Pierre" (chimpanzee), 171

Brazil, monkeys of, 43

Broom, Robert, 178

Bush-babies. See Galagos

Callithricidae (family of primates), chart 18-19

Callosities. See Skin pads

Canine teeth: adaptations for, 38; of baboons, 116, 117, 134; of early man, 178-179; of gibbons, 135; influence on leadership, 116

Captivity, adaptations to, 40-42, 51, 68, 70, 77, 109, 110, 133, 156, 190, 191

Capuchin monkeys, 34, 155; genealogy of, chart 18-19

Caribbean, rhesus monkeys of, 168

Carner, R. L., 63

Carpenter, C. R., 39, 61, 168

Cayo Santiago (island), monkeys of, 42, 112-113

Cebidae (family of primates), chart 18-19, map 44-45

Celebes macaque, 161

Cercopithecidae (family of primates), chart 18-19

Ceylon: langurs of, 97, 98-99, 168; macaques of, 84

Chimpanzees, 66-70; adaptations to captivity, 156; and alcoholism, 164-165; as artists, 155-156, 170, 171; body structure of, 11, 15, 182-183; communication by, 67, 150-151; "Congo", 155, 170-171; cost of, 161; discrimination of, 150, 151; eating habits of, 67, 131, 153, 154-155, 180; exhibitionism of, 68; experiments with, 132, 150, 151, 172, 173, 174, 175, 184; field studies of, 67-68, 70, 154-155; genealogy of, chart 18-19; grasping ability of, 11; grooming by, 107; group behaviour of, 110, 154-155; habitat of, map 44-45, 62; "Ham" (astronaut), 172; intelligence of, 70; and language, 70, 184; learning ability of, 68-70, 156-158, 174, 184; locomotion of, 67, 71; mating habits of, 68; nests of, 64; paintings by, 170, 171; physical characteristics of, 11, 66-67, 182-183; "Pierre Brassau", 170, 171; protective tactics of, 153; "rain dance" of, 68; reaction to strangers, 131-133; sex differences of, 38; social groups of, 107; and space experiments, 172, 173; of Tanzania, 67; temperament of, 67, 70, 156, 171, 182-183; testing of, 164, 165; use of tools, 153, 180; weight of, 67

China, fossils in, map 44-45, 181

Colobus monkeys, 37, 54; body structure of, 37; eating habits of, 37, diagram 131; genealogy of, chart 18-19; habitat of, map 44-45, 54, 130; predators of, 154-155; protective tactics of, 37; temperament of, 37; territorial limits of, diagram 131

Communication: of baboons, 116, 118, 119, 134; by chimpanzees, 67, 150-151; by contact, 90-92; of gibbons, 62; of gorillas, 66; by howlers (monkeys), 131; by language, 185; by langurs, chart 93; of lemurs, 88; of macaques, 132-133; of man, 182-183, 185, 186; of monkeys, 10; of orang-outangs, 62; of Peking man, 181; by spoken word, 185; of uakari monkeys, 51; of ungulates, 134

Congo (Belgian), gorillas of, 63

"Congo" (experimental chimpanzee), 155, 170-171

Coon, Carleton, 21

Crab-eating macaques, 132-133

Cretaceous, and primate genealogy, chart 18-19

Cynocephalus (dog-headed man), 152

Daily schedules of primates, 129-130

Dart, Raymond A., 178

Daubentoniidae (family of primates), chart 18-19

Death: baboons' reactions to, 134-135; fear of among primates, 132; gorillas' reactions to, 88

195

De Brazza's Monkey (guenon), *57*
Defence methods. *See* Protective tactics
DeVore, Irven, *168*
Digestive systems, adaptations of, 37, 54, 152
Discipline among baboons and macaques, 108-109, 124-125
Discrimination: ability of monkeys, 156-157; by chimpanzees, 150, 151
Disease research centre, *160-163*, 164
Douroucoulis (owl monkeys), *chart 18-19*, 130
Du Chaillu, Paul, 63
Dwarf lemurs, *12*, *chart 18-19*

East Indies: orang-outangs of, 136; tarsioids of, 13
Eating habits: of apes, compared to man's, 16; of aye-ayes, 32; of baboons, 113, 133, 140-141, *142-145*, 152, 154-155, 180, 181; of chimpanzees, 67, *153*, 154-155, 180; of colobus monkeys, 37, *diagram* 131; of gazelles, 140-141; of gibbons, 74, 130; of gorillas, 64, 67, 77, 130; of guenons, *diagram* 131; of howler monkeys, 130; of impalas, 140-141; influence on evolution, 180; influence of food availability, 36-37; influence of status, 142; of langurs, 37, 54, 89, 97, *100*, 101, 130; of lemuroids, 11; of lorises, 13, 29; of macaques, 42, 106, 133, 136, 181; of man, 154, 182, 185; of monkeys, 13-14, 15, 37, 49, 86, 130, *diagram* 131; of mouse lemurs, 24-25; of Peking man, 181; of proboscis monkeys, 53; of sea otters, 154; of squirrel monkeys, 48; of tarsiers, *22-23*; of tree shrews, 20; of vervets, 152; of woodpecker-finches, 154
Ecuador, woolly monkeys of, *176*
Egypt, baboons of, 58-59, *180*, *187*
Elephants, *145*
Emlen, John, 63
Emotions. *See* Temperament
Emperor tamarin (monkey), *chart 18-19*
Environment, influence upon man, 158
Eocene, and primate genealogy, *chart 18-19*
Ethiopia, baboons of, 58, 113
Europe, fossils in, *map 44-45*, 181
Evolution, 10-11, 15-16; of body structure size, 16; development of sex adaptations, 182; effects of isolation on, 35-36; of gorillas, 82-83; importance of exogamy on, 185-186; influence of base camps, 182; influence of eating habits, 180; influence of hunting, 155, 181-182; influence of language, 183; in locomotion of primates, 12; of man, 82, 83, 151-158, 177-186; of primates, 17, *chart 18-19*, 21; of prosimians, 11; relationships of man and ape, 16; of tarsioids, 13; theories of, *178*, 179, 180
Exogamy, 185-186
Experience and learning among primates, 153, 156

Experiments: on alcoholism, *164-165*; with artistic ability of monkeys, 155-156; on body disorders, *160*; with body structure, 162; in brain activity, 159; with chimpanzees, 132, *150*, 151, *172*, 173, *174*, *175*, 184; with isolation, 157-158; with language, 184; in learning ability, *157*; with macaques, 86-87, 132-133, 164-165; on monkeys' emotional make-up, 7; with mother-child relationships, 86-87, 90-91, 158; with orang-outangs, *165*; in physical disorders, *162*, *163*; with pure oxygen, *173*; with rats, 90; with rhesus monkeys, *157*, 161; with sex instincts, 91-92; on social behaviour, 164, 165; for space travel, 159, *172*, 173, *174*, *175*, 177; with surgery, *160*, *162*, *163*

Faces: of chimpanzees, *182-183*; of infant baboons, *89*
Feet, structure of, *14*
Females, status among, 110-111, 118, 119, 121, 123
Field studies: of baboons, 89, 111, 114, 131, 133-134, 141, 154, 168-169; of chimpanzees, 67-68, 70, 154-155; as clues to man's history, 151; of gibbons, 61; of gorillas, 63, 64-66, 90, 135-136; of group behaviour, 168-169; of howlers, 39-40, 168; importance of, 168; of India, 168; of langurs, 87-89, *132*, 136, 168; of leadership determination, 110; of macaques, 106, 111, 132, 168; of monkeys, 87, 90, 112-113, 135; of orang-outangs, 190; of proboscis monkeys, 168, *169*; of protective tactics, 141; purpose of, 7; of rhesus monkeys, 168
Finger-nails, adaptations of, 10
Florida, wild-life reservation of, 190
Fossils, *map 44-45*; of *Australopithecus*, *178*; in Africa, *178*, 179, 181; in China, 181; in Europe, 181; in Java, 180-181; in Johannesburg, *178*; of man, 178-181; of monkeys, 43, 152; of primates, 18-19; of prosimians, 11; of tarsioids, 13
Fruit-flies, and space travel, 173
Fungus spores, and space travel, 173

Galagidae (family of primates), *chart 18-19*
Galagos, or bush-babies (lemurs), 12, *17*; genealogy of, *chart 18-19*; habitat of, *map 44-45*; locomotion of, 12, 28
Gazelles, *140-141*
Gelada baboons, 58
Genealogy of primates, *chart 18-19*
Genera: of apes, 15; of monkeys, 35; number of, *chart 18-19*; of lemurs, 24
Gestation periods of primates, *chart 86*
Gibbons, 60, 61, 62, 72-73, *74*, *75*; body structure of, 15, *62*, *63*, *64*, *135*; canine teeth of, *135*; communication by, 62; eating habits of, 74, 130; field

studies of, 61; genealogy of, *chart 18-19*; habitat of, *map 44-45*, 62, 71, 130; infants of, *74*; intelligence of, 62; locomotion of, *60*, 61-64, *72-73*, *75*, 86, 130; physical characteristics of, 63, *62-64*, 72-73, *74*, *75*, *135*; protective tactics of, 131, 135; sex differences of, 38, *135*; sex hostility of, 62; skin pads of, 64; sleeping habits of, 74; taxonomy of, 62; territorial limits of, *chart* 130; weight of, 67
Giraffes, *145*
Golden langurs, *54*
Gombe Stream Chimpanzee Reserve, 67
Goodall, Jane, 67, 68, 153, 154
Gorillas, 63-66; of Africa, 63, 136; apparent ferocity of, 63, 66; as artists, 155; body structure of, *65*, *82-83*, 90; chest beating by, 64, *66-67*; communication by, 66; death reactions of, 88; diseases of, 164; eating habits of, 64, 67, 77, 130, 131; evolution of, 82-83; field studies of, 63, 64-66, 90, 135-136; genealogy of, *chart 18-19*; grasping ability of, 82; grooming of, 107; group behaviour of, 65-67, *76*, 77, 110, 114; growth patterns of, *chart 86*; habitat of, *map 44-45*, 62, 63, 71; infants of, 66, 77, *78*, 86, *90-91*; intelligence of, 68, 69; leadership among, 65, 66, 108, 111; locomotion of, *65*, 67, 82, *90-91*; lowland, 63; maturation of, *chart 86*; mountain, 63, 65, *66-67*, 136; nests of, 64, 65, *79*; physical characteristics, 63, *65*; at play *90-91*; protective adaptations of, 41; protective tactics of, 41, *66*, 67, 135, 152-153; reactions to strangers, 131-133; sex differences in, 114; sexual maturity, *chart 86*; silver-back, 65, 66; similarity to man, 65; sleeping habits of, 64-65; social groups of, 107, 110; social maturity, *chart 86*; temperament of, 65-67, 77; territorial limits of, *chart* 130; testing of, 164, 165; and use of weapons, 152-153
Grasping ability of primates, 10-14; adaptations for, *10-11*, 13-14; of chimpanzees, *11*; of gorillas, 82; importance for infant monkeys, 86; of lorises, *10*; of macaques, *11*; of marmosets, *11*; of Peking man, 181; of pottos, 31; of tarsiers, *10*; of tree shrews, 10
Grooming methods of primates, 107; by baboons, 107, 115, 122; by chimpanzees, 107; by gorillas, 107; by macaques, 107, 168; by pottos, 31
Ground living, adaptations to, 38, 135, 152, 179
Group behaviour: adaptations in, 185; of apes, 129-130, 131-133; of baboons, 40-41, *104-105*, 111, 113, 115, 118, 119, 124, 125, 133-135, 137, *diagram* 138-139, 140-141, *146-147*, 154, 180-182; of chimpanzees, 110, 154-155; field studies of, 168-169; of gibbons, 62; of gorillas, 65-67, *76*, 77, 110, 114; of howlers, 131; of indri, 25; of langurs, 53, 87-

90, 93, *96-97*, 132; of lemurs, 25; and locomotion, 134; of macaques, 114, 135, 181-182; of man, 182, 185, 186; of monkeys, 10, 102, 129-130, 135, *188*; of orang-outangs, 62; of rhesus monkeys, 167; of tree shrews, 21
Growth patterns, 85-103, *chart 86*; of baboons, 89, 119; of gorillas, *chart 86*; of guenons, *chart 86*; of langurs, *chart 93*, 95, 102; of man, *chart 86*, 183-184, 186
Guenon monkeys, 35, 37, *56-57*; eating habits of, *diagram* 131; genealogy of, *chart 18-19*; growth patterns of, *chart 86*; habitat of, *map 44-45*; maturation of, *chart 86*; locomotion of, 57; physical characteristics of, 57; sexual maturity, *chart 86*; social maturity, *chart 86*; territorial limits of, *diagram* 131

Habitat of primates: of apes, 177; of baboons, 58, 113; of chimpanzees, 62; of colobus monkeys, 54, 130; of galagos, *map 44-45*; of gibbons, 62, 71, 130; of gorillas, 62, 63, 71; of howlers, 130; of langurs, 54; of lorises, *map 44-45*; of macaques, 106-107, 136; of marmoset monkeys, 43; of squirrel monkeys, 48, 49; of New World monkeys, 36-42; of Old World monkeys, 36-42; of orang outangs, 62, 130; of pottos, *map 44-45*; of prosimians, *map 44-45*; of uakari monkeys, 50
Haddow, A. J., 92
Hall, K.R.L., 131, 135, 153
"Ham" (chimpanzee astronaut), *172*
Hamadryad baboons, *chart 18-19*, 40-42, *58-59*, 110, 113, *187*
Hamburg, David A., 89
Hanuman, the monkey god, 188, 189
Harlow, Harry, 86, 87, 90, 91, 156-158, 166-167
Harrisson, Barbara, *169*
Hindus: monkey dance of, *189*; monkey worship by, 136, 188
Holloman Air Force Base, N.M., and space experiments, 173, *174*, *175*
Hominidae (family of primates), *chart 18-19*
Hominids (early family of mankind), 178-179
Howler monkeys, *47*, 130-133; communication by, 131; eating habits of, 130; field studies of, 39-40, 168; genealogy of, *chart 18-19*; group behaviour of, 131; habitat of, 130; locomotion of, 130; temperament of, 39-40; territorial limits of, *chart* 130
Hunting: ability of Peking man, 181; importance in human evolution, 155, 181-182; influence on sex life, 185
Hylobatidae (family of primates), *chart 18-19*

Impalas, 140, *141*
India: field studies of, 168; langurs of, 97, 130, *map 132*, 136; monkeys of, 188

Indri (lemur), *25;* genealogy of, *chart* 18-19; group behaviour of, 25

Indriidae (family of primates), 11, *chart* 18-19, 24, 152; physical characteristics of, *152*

Infant dependency of primates, *chart* 86

Infants: of baboons, *89,* 94, *120-125,* 134, 146; causes of neuroses in, 157-158; of gibbons, *74;* of gorillas, 66, *77, 78,* 86, *90-91;* importance of grasping ability, 86; of langurs, 89, 92, 93, *95,* 97-99, 101, *168;* of macaques, *84,* 86-87; of man, 182-184; of monkeys, 10, 85-94; of Peking man, 184; of pottos, *31;* protective tactics for, 88; of rhesus monkeys, 86-87, 166-167; of sifakas, *26;* temperament in monkeys, 90

Insectivores, genealogy of, *chart* 18-19

Intelligence: of chimpanzees, 70; of gibbons, 62; of gorillas, 68, 69; laboratory tests for, 15, 68, 69; of monkeys, 35, 69

Ischial callosities. *See* Skin pads

Isolation: effects on evolution, 35-36; effects on primates, 157-158

Japan, research centres of, 168, 190

Jamaica, fossils from, *map* 44-45

Java, fossils from, 180-181

Jay, Phyllis, 87, 88, 110, 136, 158, *168*

Johannesburg, fossils of, 178

Kenya, baboons of, *104-105,* 114

Kirunga Range, Africa, 65

Kohts, N., *150,* 151

Kortlandt, Adriaan, 70

Kudu (antelope), *144*

Kyushu, macaques of, 105-114

Language: chimpanzees' use of, 70, *184;* experiments with, 184; influence on evolution, 183; man's use of, 182-183, 185

Langurs, 87-89, *96-97,* 99; of Asia, 54; body structure of, 37; of Borneo, 53; of Ceylon, 97, 98-99, *168;* communication by, *chart* 93; eating habits of, 37, 54, 89, 97, *100,* 101, 130; field studies of, 87-89, 132, 136, 168; genealogy of, *chart* 18-19; as gods, 54, 136; golden, *54;* group behaviour of, 53, 87-90, 93, *96-97,* 132; growth patterns of, *chart* 93, 95, 102; habitat of, *map* 44-45, 54; of India, 97, 130, *map* 132, 136; infants of, 89, 92, 93, *95,* 97-99, 101, *168;* leadership among, 88, 94, 108, *110;* learning ability of, 90, *chart* 93, 97; locomotion of, 37, *97, 102-103,* 130; mating habits of, 93, 109-110; mother-child relationships of, 88-89, 95, *98-99, 100,* 101; number of species of, 36; physical characteristics of, 95; proboscis monkeys, *52-53;* protective tactics of, 37, *103,* 131; reactions to strangers, 131-133; sex differences in, 93, 94, 101,

102; similarity to man, 92, 136; sleeping habits of, 108; snub-nosed, *53;* social groups of, *101,* 110; species of, 36; status among, 110, 136; temperament of, 37, 53, 88, 93, 110; territorial limits of, *chart* 130, *map* 132; weaning of, 92-93

LaSalle, Dr. Marjorie, *162*

Leadership among primates: among baboons, 94, *111,* 116, 118, 119, 146; basis for, 107-109; determination of, 110-112, 116-119; among gorillas, 65, 66, 108, 111; influence of canine teeth, 116; among langurs, 88, 94, 108, *110;* among macaques, 105-106, 111, 112, 132, 133; in monkeys, 10; similarity to governments of man, 111

Leakey, Louis, 67, 178-179

Learning ability: of animals, 70; of baboons, 89, 134, 141, 180; of chimpanzees, 68-70, 156; 158, *174, 184;* experiments in, *157;* of gorillas, *90-91;* of langurs, 90, *chart* 93, 97; of man, 156-158, 183; of monkeys, 89, 90; of Peking man, 181, 184; of rhesus monkeys, *157*

Leg musculature, man and gorilla, 65

Lemuridae (family of primates), *chart* 18-19

Lemuroids, 11-13, 24, 32, *map* 44-45. *See also* Daubentoniidae; Indriidae; Lemurs; Lorises

Lemurs: brain of, *13;* communication by, 88; dwarf, 12, adaptations for temperature, *12; chart* 18-19; genealogy of, *chart* 18-19; genera of, 24; group behaviour of, 25; indri, 152; of Madagascar, 8, 9, 24, *map* 44-45, 152; mouse lemurs, 11-12, *24-25,* 32; pottos, 12-13, *31;* research on, *160;* ring-tailed, *8,* 9; ruffed, *chart* 18-19; sense organs of, 13; social groups of, 25; status among, 88

Limb proportions, man and gibbon, *64*

"Lizzie" (macaque astronaut), *173*

Locomotion: adaptations for, *62, 63, 64, 65,* 82; of Australopithecines, 181; of baboons, 37, 121; of chimpanzees, 67, *71;* comparisons in, 15; evolution of, 12; of galagos, 12, 28; of gibbons, 60-61, 62-73, 75, 86, 130; of gorillas, 65, 67, 82, *90-91,* 130; of groups and communities, 134; of guenons, 57; of howlers, 130; of indri, 25; of langurs, 37, *97, 102-103,* 130; of lemuroids, 11, 12, 24; of lorises, 12-13, 28, 29; of macaques, 62, 82; of man, 42, *64, 65,* 82, 178, 184; of monkeys, 12, 14-15, 49, 82, 86, 89, 135; or orang-outangs, 62, 63, *80,* 81; of Peking man, 181; of pottos, 12-13, *31;* of prosimians, 12; for protection, 92; of sifakas, 26, 27; of sloths, 28-29; and speciation in primates, 10; of tarsiers, *14,* 23; of uakari monkeys, 50

Loeres (lorises), *28,* 29

London Zoo, baboons of, 40,

110

Lorises, 12-13, *28, 29;* body structure of, *10;* eating habits of, 13, 29; genealogy of, *chart* 18-19; grasping ability of, *10;* habitat of, *map* 44-45; locomotion of, 12-13, 28, 29; of Malaysia, *29;* physical characteristics of, *10,* 29

Lorisoids, 28

Lowland gorilla, 63

Macaque monkeys, *84,* 94; adaptations to captivity, 133; adaptations to ground living, 152; adaptations to man's residential areas, *188;* Barbary ape, *map* 44-45; brain of, *13;* body structure of, *11, 62, 82-83;* bonnet, *18;* of Cayo Santiago, 42, 112-113; Celebes, *161;* of Ceylon, 84; communication of, 132, 133; crab-eating species of, 132-133; discipline among, 108-109; eating habits of, 42, 106, 133, 136, 181; effects of isolation upon, 157-158; experiments with, 86-87, 132-133, 164-165; field studies of, 106, 111, 132, 168; genealogy, *chart* 18-19; as gods, 136, *188;* grasping ability of, *11;* grooming by, 107, 168; group behaviour of, 114, 135, 181-182; habitat of, *map* 44-45, 106-107, 136; infants of, 84, 86-87; of Kyushu, 105-114; leadership among, 105-106, 111, 112, 132, 133; "Lizzie" (astronaut), *173;* locomotion of, 62, 82; mating habits of, 109; nasal structure of, *36;* number of species of, 36; physical characteristics of, *11, 36,* 106; pigtail, *graph* 108, 132-133, 135, 152-153; reactions to strangers, 131-133; on Santiago (island), Puerto Rico, 40-41; sense organs of, 13; sex differences in, 114; sleeping habits of, 135, 181; social groups of, 42, 94, 105-111, 181-182; species of, 36; status among, 42, 106-107; of Takasakiyama (island), 105-111, 114; temperament of, 41, *graph* 108, 112, 132; territorial limits of, 130-131; and use of weapons, 152-153. *See* Rhesus monkeys.

Madagascar: aye-ayes of, *32, 33;* lemurs of, 8, 9, 24, *map* 44-45, 152; prosimians of, 11

Malaysia: lorises of, *29;* tree shrews of, 20

Malinow, René, *162-163*

Man: adaptability of, 42; birth patterns of, 184; body structure of, *14, 64, 65, 82-83,* 178, 183; canine teeth of, 178-179; daily schedules of, 129; early man in Africa, 177-178; eating habits of, 154, 182, 185; environment and, 158; evolution of, 82, 83, 151-158, 177-186; fossils of, 178-181; genealogy of, *chart* 18-19; group behaviour of, 182, 185, 186; growth patterns of, *chart* 86, 183-184, 186; infants of, 182-184; and language, 182-183, 185; learning ability of, 156-158, 183; loco-

motion of, 42, *64, 65,* 82, 178, 184; maternal instincts of, 158; maturation of, *chart* 86; mother-child relationships of, 167, 184; Peking man, 181, 184; physical characteristics of, *14, 64, 65,* 178; as a predator, 136, 154, 180-181; protective tactics of, 167, 179, 180, 182, 185; sense organs of, 13; sex differences of, 182, 184; sex hostility of, 185; sex instincts of, 184-185; sexual maturity, *chart* 86; similarity to apes, 16, 178, 186; similarity to monkeys, 87, 159, 187; social groups of, 182, 185, 186; social maturity, *chart* 86; speciation of, 186; temperament of, 158; territorial limits of, *chart* 130; and tools, 183; traditions of, 186; unique position of, 151, 178; and weapons, 152-153

Mangabey monkeys, *chart* 18-19, 37, *map* 44-45

Marmoset monkeys, *chart* 18-19, 43; grasping ability of, *11; map* 44-45

Martin, William C., 61

Maternal instincts, in primates, 89, 99, 158

Mating habits: of baboons, 113; of chimpanzees, 68; of langurs, 93, 109-110; of macaques, 109; of rhesus monkeys, 109, 112-113

Maturation, comparisons, *chart* 86

Merfield, Fred, 111

Migration, of prosimians, 11

Miocene, and primate genealogy, *chart* 18-19

Monkey dance, Hindu, *189*

Monkey worship, Hindu, 136, 188

Monkeys, 35-59; of Africa, 35, 36-37, 56-57; artistic ability of, *170, 171;* of Asia, 36-37; of Barro Colorado Island, 39-40; birth patterns of, 31, 85, 90; of Borneo, 168, *169;* of Brazil, 43; capuchins, *34,* 155, *190;* colobus, *see* Colobus monkeys; communication by, 10; daily schedules of, 129-130; differences in, 35-38; discrimination ability of, 156-157; douroucoulis, 130; eating habits of, 13-14, 15, 37, 49, 86, 130, *diagram* 131; of Ecuador, *176;* effects of isolation upon, 157-158; experiments with, 7, 91-92; field studies of, 87, 90, 112-113, 135; as food, 177; fossils of, 43, 152; genera of, 35; grasping ability of, 14, 86; as gods, 136, 188, 189; group behaviour of, 10, 102, 129-130, 135, 188; growth of species, 14; growth patterns of, *chart* 86; guenons, *see* Guenon monkeys; habitat of, 36-42, *map* 44-45, 48, 49, 54, 130; howlers, *see* Howler monkeys; of India, 188; infants of, 10, 85-94; intelligence of, 35, 69; leadership among, 10; learning ability of, 89, 90; locomotion of, 12, 14-15, 49, 82, 86, 89, 135; mangabeys, 37; marmosets, *11, 43;* maternal instincts of, 89, 158; maturation of, *chart*

86; New World, *see* New World monkeys; nostrils of, *36;* number of species of, 35, 47; Old World, *see* Old World monkeys; olive colobus, 130; owl, 130; of Panama, 39-40, 168; patas, 135; physical characteristics of, 14, 16, *36,* 38, *39,* 50, 53, 54, 135; predators of, 37-38, 49, 154-155; proboscis, *52-53,* 168, *169;* protective adaptations of, 41; rehabilitation for, 168, 169; relationship to tarsiers, 13; rhesus, *see* Rhesus monkeys; Schmidt's white-nosed, *57;* sense organs of 13, 14; similarity to man, 87, 159, 187; skin pads of, *38,* 39, 64, *128,* 129; sleeping habits of, 39, 129, 130, 135; social groups of, 9-10, 41, 49, 92; of South America, 36-37, 39, 130, 131; space experiments with, *172,* 173; species of, 35, 43, 47; spider monkeys, *39, 46,* 131; squirrel monkeys, *48-49;* surgery for, *160, 162-163;* temperament of, 90, 158; territorial limits of, *chart* 130; traditions of, 130-131; uakaris, *50, 51;* vervets, 152; weaning of, 87; woolly, *36,* 47, *176;* of Zanzibar, *55. See also* individual kinds

Moorehead, Alan, 65

Morris, Desmond, 155-156, 170-171

Mother-child relationships, 85-94; of baboons, *89,* 110-111, 120-121; experiments with, 86-87, 90-91, 158; of langurs, 88-89, *95, 98-99, 100,* 101; of man, 167, 184; of rhesus monkeys, *166-167*

Mother substitutes, 86

Mountain gorillas, 63, 65, 136; chest beating of, *66-67;* protective tactics of, *66-67;* territorial limits of, *chart* 130

Mouse lemurs, 11-12, *24-25,* 32

Movement. *See* Locomotion

Multiple births in primates, 85

Murchison Falls National Park, patas monkeys of, 135

Nairobi Park, baboons of, *89,* 134

National parks: Albert, 63; Gombe Stream Chimpanzee Reserve, 67; Murchison Falls, 135; Nairobi, 89, 134

Nests: of aye-ayes, 32; of chimpanzees, 64; of gorillas, 64, 65, *79;* of mouse lemurs, 24; of orang-outangs, 64

Neuroses, causes of, 157

New World monkeys, 15, 43, 48-49; genealogy of, *chart* 18-19; habitat of, 36-42, *map* 44-45; nostrils of, *36;* number of species of, 47; physical characteristics of, *36;* prehensile tails of, *39*

North Africa, fossils of, 181

North America, fossils of, *map* 44-45

Nostrils, of New and Old World monkeys, *36*

Old World monkeys: 15, 37-43, 52-59, 64; genealogy of, *chart* 18-19; habitat of, 36-42, *map* 44-45; nostrils of, *36;* physical

characteristics of, *36;* skin pads of, *38,* 39, *128*

Olduvai Gorge, fossils from, 178-179

Oligocene, and primate genealogy, *chart* 18-19

Olive colobus monkeys, 130

Orang-outangs, 62-64, *80, 81;* adaptations to captivity, 190, 191; as artists, 155; behavioural testing of, 164, 165; body structure of, 15, *63;* of Borneo, 63; communication by, 62; cost of, 161; of East Indies, 136; experiments with, *165;* field studies of, 190; genealogy of, *chart* 18-19; group behaviour of, 62; habitat of, *map* 44-45, 62, 130; locomotion of, 62, 63, *80, 81;* nests of, 64; physical characteristics of, 62, 63; possible extinction of, 136; sex differences of, 38, 62; skin pads of, 38-39; of Sumatra, 63; temperament of, 67, 81

Oregon research centre, *160-163,* 164

Owl monkeys, 130

Palaeocene, and primate genealogy, *chart* 18-19

Panama, monkeys of, 39-40, 168

Patas monkeys, 135

Peking, fossils from, 181

Peking man, 181, 184

Pen-tailed tree shrews, *20*

Physical characteristics: of *Australopithecus, 178;* of aye-ayes, 32, *33;* of baboons, 38, 40, 58, *89,* 116, *117, 134;* of chimpanzees, *11,* 66-67, *182-183;* of gibbons, 61, *62,* 63, 64, 72-73, *74, 75, 135;* of gorillas, 63, *65;* of guenons, 57; of hands, *10-11;* of indriidae, 24, 152; of langurs, 95; of lemuroids, 11, 32; of lorises, *10,* 29; of macaques, *11, 36,* 106; of man, *14,* 15, *64,* 65, *178;* of marmosets, *11;* of monkeys, 14, 16, *36,* 38, 50, 53, 54, 135; of mouse lemurs, 11-12, 24; nostril structures, *36;* of orang-outangs, 62, *63;* of pottos, *30, 31;* of prosimians, 12, 14; of sifakas, 26-27; of sloths, 29; of spider monkeys, *39;* of tarsiers, *10,* 13, *14,* 15, *23;* of tree shrews, *10,* 20-21; of woolly monkeys, *36*

Physiological research, *160,* 161, 165

Pigtail macaques, 164-165

Pleistocene, and primate genealogy, *chart* 18-19

Pliocene, and primate genealogy, *chart* 18-19

Pongidae (family of primates), *chart* 18-19

Pope, Alexander, quote from, 151

Pottos (lemurs): 12-13, 28-29; genealogy of, *chart* 18-19; grasping ability of, 31; grooming by, 31; habitat of, *map* 44-45; infants of, *31;* locomotion of, 12-13, *31;* physical characteristics of, *30, 31*

Predators: adaptations against, 115, 152-153, 180-181; baboons as, *142, 143;* man as, 136, 139, 146, *148-149;* man as, 136, 154, 180-181; of monkeys, 37-38, 49, 154-155; protective tactics against, 145

Prehensile tails, *39, 46,* 47

Primate Research Group, Japan, 168

Primates: experience and learning among, 153, 156; genealogy of, *chart* 18-19; origin of word, 17; research centres for, 7, 161, 168, 190; species of, 10. *See also* individual kinds

Primatology, 9; founding father of, 69; research studies in, 190

Proboscis monkeys, *52-53,* 168, *169*

Prosimians (lemurs), 11-14, 28; evolution of, 11; fossils of, 11; genealogy of, *chart* 18-19; habitat of, *map* 44-45; largest, 25; locomotion of, 12; of Madagascar, 11; migrations of, 11; physical characteristics of, 12, 14; species of, 11; traits of, 9

Protective tactics of primates, 37, 39, 41, 58, 88, 92, 94, *103,* 131-135, 179; adaptations for, 37-38, 41, 94, 179; of baboons, 37, 116, 121, 131, 134, 135, 140-141, *146-149,* 152-153, 182; of chimpanzees, 153; of colobus monkeys, 37; and co-operation among animals, 134, 140-141; of early man, 180; field studies of, 141; of gazelles, 140-141; of gibbons, 131, 135; of gorillas, 41, *66-67,* 135, 152-153; group formations for, *diagram* 139; of impalas, 140-141; for infants, 88; of langurs, 37, *103,* 131; of macaques, 39, *graph* 108, 132-133, 135, 152-153; of man, 167, 179, 182, 185; against predators, 145; of rhesus monkeys, 159, 166-167, *168*

Psychological research on primates, 156-158, 187

Puerto Rico, monkey colony of, 168

"Rain dance" of chimpanzees, 68

Ranges. *See* Territorial limits of primates

Rats, experiments with, 90

Rehabilitation, for monkeys, 168, 169

Research: archaeological, 178-179; on disease, *160-163,* 164; physiological, *160,* 161, 165; psychological, 156-158, 187; on primates, 7, 132, 159, 161, 168, 190

Reynolds, Frances, 67

Reynolds, Vernon, 67

Rhesus monkeys: adaptations of, 136; brain activity of, 159; of the Caribbean, *168;* of Cayo Santiago, 112-113; cost of, 161; eating habits of, 136; experiments with, *157,* 161; field studies of, *168;* as gods, 136; group behaviour of, 167; habitat of, 136; infants of, 86-87, 166-167; isolation, effects of on, 158; learning ability of, *157;* mating habits of, 109, 112-113; mother-child relationships of, *166-167;* protective tactics of, *159,* 166-167, *168;* reactions to strangers, 131-133; research on, 159, 161; sex instincts of, 167; and space travel, 173; surgery for, *162-163;* temperament of, *graph* 108, 166-167. *See* Macaque monkeys

Rhodesia, baboons of Western, 144, 145

Ring-tailed lemurs, *8,* 9

Ripley, Suzanne, *168*

Rousseau, Jean-Jacques, 129

Ruffed lemur, *chart* 18-19

Sade, Don, 112

Sakis (monkeys), *chart* 18-19

Santiago (island), Puerto Rico, macaques of, 40-41

Schaller, George, 63, 64, 65, 66, 88, 90, 92, 135, 136; drawings by, *90-91*

Schmidt's white-nosed monkey, 5

Sea otters, 154

Seasons, adaptations for, 54

Sense organs: adaptations of, 10, 12; of apes, 13; of aye-ayes, 32; centres in the brain, *13;* of gazelles, 140-141; of impalas, 140-141; of lemurs, *13;* of macaques, *13;* of man, 13; of monkeys, 13, 14; of tarsiers, *15* 23; of tree shrews, *13,* 20

Sex differences: adaptations in, 38; of baboons, 38, 94, *134;* of chimpanzees, 38; of gibbons, *135;* of gorillas, 114; of langurs 93, 94, 101, 102; of macaques, 114; of man, 182, 184; of orang-outangs, 38, 62

Sex hostility: in baboons, 40; in gibbons, 62; in man, 185

Sex instincts: adaptations in, 184-185; experiments with monkeys', 91-92; of man, 184-185; of rhesus monkeys, 16

Sexual maturity, *chart* 86

Shrews, tree. *See* Tree shrews

Sifakas (lemurs), *chart* 18-19, *26,*

Silver-back gorillas, 65, 66

Skin pads: of baboons, *128,* 129; of gibbons, 64; of monkeys, *38,* 39, 64; of orang-outangs, 38-39

Sleeping habits: of aye-ayes, 32; of baboons, 113, *128,* 129, 135, 181; of gibbons, 74; of gorillas, 64-65; of langurs, 108; of macaques, 135, 181; of monkeys, 39, 130, 135; of mouse lemurs, 24, 32

Sloths, 28-29

Smell, brain centre of, 13

Snub-nosed langur, *53*

Social behaviour, experiments on 164, 165

Social groups among primates: adaptations of, 107, 113; of apes, 129-130; of baboons, 40, 42, 94, 110, *111,* 113, 121-123, 144, 145, 181-182; basis for, 109; break-up of, 114; of chimpanzees, 107; comparison of monkeys' and man's, 186; formations of, 114; of gorillas, 10 110; of langurs, *101, 110;* of le murs, 25; of macaques, 42, 94, 105-111, 181-182; of man, 182 185, 186; of monkeys, 9-10, 41 49, 92; similarity to man's, 133-134; and territorial limits, 130-131

Social maturity, *chart* 86

South America: fossils of, *map* 44-45; monkeys of, 36-37, 39, 130, 131

Space travel, experiments for, 15 *172,* 173, 174, *175,* 177

Speciation: by grasping ability, 10, 11, 12, 13-14; of man, 186 of tarsiers, 23

Species: definition of, 35; growth in, 14; of langurs, 36; of living primates, 10; of macaques, 36; of monkeys, 35, 43, 47; of prosimians, 11; of tarsioids, 13; territorial limits of, *diagram* 131

Spider monkeys, *chart* 18-19, *39, 46,* 131

Squirrel monkeys, *chart* 18, *48-49*

Status: among baboons, 42, 107, *111,* 118, 119, 124; of females, 110-111, 118, 119, 121, 123; influence on diet, 142; among langurs, *110,* 136; among lemurs, 88; among macaques, 42, 106-107

Strawberry Canyon, research centre of, 132

Substitute mothers: for pottos, *31;* for rhesus monkeys, *166-167*

Sumatra, orang-outangs of, 63

Surgery, for monkeys, 160, *162-163*

Survival, adaptations for, 131

Sweden, chimpanzees of, 170, 171

Tails, prehensile, *39, 46,* 47

Takasakiyama (island), macaques of, 105-111, 114

Tamarins (monkeys), *chart* 18-19

Tanganyika, fossils from 178-179

Tanzania, chimpanzees of, 67

Tarsiers (lemuroids), 13, *14-15, 22-23;* eating habits of, 22-23;

genealogy of, *chart* 18-19; grasping ability of, *10;* habitat of, *map* 44-45; locomotion of, *14,* 23; physical characteristics of, *10,* 13, *14, 15,* 23; relationship to monkeys, 13; sense organs of, *15,* 23; skull of, *15,* speciation in, 23; vision of, *15*

Tarsioids (lemuroids), 13

Taxonomy: of aye-ayes, 32; of gibbons, 62

Teeth. *See* Canine teeth

Temperament: adaptations in, 41; of baboons, 40, 41, 107, 108, 111, 112, 113, 123; of chimpanzees, 67, 70, 156, 171, *182-183;* of colobus monkeys, 37; of gorillas, 65-67, 77; of howlers, 39-40; of infant monkeys, 90; of langurs, 37, 53, 88, 93, 110; of macaques, 41, *graph* 108, 112, 132; of man, 158; of monkeys, 90, 158; of orang-outangs, 67, 81; of rhesus monkeys, 166-167; of tree shrews, 21; of uakari monkeys, 51

Temperatures, adaptations to, *12*

Territorial limits of primates, *chart* 130, *diagram* 131, *map* 132, 137, 144-145, 181, 185

Toe-nails, adaptations of, 10

Tools: and chimpanzees, *153,* 180; and man, 183

Traditions: of man, 186; of meat eating, 154-155; of monkeys and apes, 130-131

Tree living, adaptations to, 10, 12, 16, 94

Tree shrews, 10-11, 28; brain, *13;* body structure of, *10;* of Borneo, *20;* common, *20;* eating habits of, 20; genealogy of, *chart* 18-19; grasping ability of, *10;* group behaviour of, 21; habitat, *map* 44-45; of Malaysia, *20;* pen-tailed, *20;* physical characteristics of, *10,* 20-21; sense organs of, 13, 20; temperament of, 21; tupai, 20; vision of, 21

Tupai (tree shrews), 20

Tupaiidae (family of primates), *chart* 18-19

Uakari monkeys, *chart* 18-19, *50, 51*

Uganda: gorillas of, 63; patas monkeys of, 135

Ungulates, 134

University of California: experiments with monkeys at, 132-133; fossil research of, 178

University of Wisconsin, experiments with monkeys at, 86, 156-157

University of Witwatersrand, archaeological researchers of, 178

Vervets (monkeys), 152

Vision: of baboons, 140-141; brain centres of, *13;* of tarsiers, *15;* of tree shrews, 21

Wart-hogs, *144-145*

Washburn, Sherwood L., 89, 132-133, 178

Weaning: of langurs, 92-93; of monkeys, 87

Weapons, use by man and other primates, 152-153

Weights: of chimpanzees, 67; of gibbons, 62, 74

White-headed saki, *chart* 18-19

White-nosed monkey, Schmidt's, *57*

Wisconsin Regional Primate Center, 166-167

Woodpecker-finch (bird), 154

Woolly monkeys, *chart* 18-19, *36, 47, 176*

Yerkes, Robert M., 69

Yerkes Regional Primate Center, Georgia, 164-165

Zambia, baboons of, 114

Zanzibar, monkeys of, *55*

Zebras, *144-145*

Ӿ

Typesetting by Hazell, Watson & Viney Ltd., Aylesbury
Smeets Lithographers, Weert, Printed in Holland
Bound by Proost and Brandt N.V., Amsterdam